CONTENTS

D0002936

INTRODUCTION

I love the Bible. I hope you do too. That's the major reason for this book—love. You see, I was blessed with parents who taught me to love Scripture. Oh, I *learned* it—we spent lots of Sunday afternoons playing "Bible baseball" and other quiz games—but we also had a lot of fun with it. The Bible is a very creative book, and my parents were quick to teach me that. I learned to love its wit, its quirks, its jokes.

Love comes in different forms. You might have a prim and proper aunt who comes over for Thanksgiving dinner. You love and respect her greatly, but you're afraid to fool around in her presence. A lot of people treat the Bible the same way. Nothing wrong with that—but if that describes you, you won't enjoy this book.

But maybe there's someone else you love—a cousin or a classmate or a pal—someone you can play touch football with. That's the kind of love I have for the Bible. I want to wrestle with it, to laugh with it, to make it a part of my life. I want to imagine its events happening today, and today's technology happening back then. What if I could talk with Moses or Peter or that guy who got his ear cut off? What if? If you love the Bible like that, I think you'll love this book.

Let me apologize in advance if anything here offends you. That's not my intention. I'm never laughing *at* the Bible in disrespect. I'm trying to laugh *with* it. And with you.

The book has three sections, which you might consider Easy, Medium, and Hard. But I've fought the temptation to offer scoring in this book. It's a book to have fun with, not to judge yourself with. But if the first section seems too easy for you, move on. If the last section is too tough, take a guess and learn from it. Maybe next time through you'll get it.

Throughout these chapters I sprinkle Amazing Facts, Brain Stuff, Crazy Ads, Dumb Jokes, and Extras. You'll get the hang of that. Of course, the Crazy Ads may throw you. I'm just thinking creatively . . . what if biblical events occurred in the modern marketplace? That's the same idea as the TV Listings at the end of the chapters. What if these pages were televised?

My basic Bible version is the New Living Translation (NLT).

I find it offers a freshness while remaining true to the original intentions of Scripture. (And it's published by Tyndale House, the publisher of *this* book.) Occasionally, however, the New International Version offers a familiarity you might need, so I'll revert to that. On occasion I even tap into the King James Version and the New Revised Standard Version.

I want to thank Lauree Padgett for her dumb jokes, Deb Stranahan for her questions, and Victor Kore for his patience. And Mom and Dad for instilling in me a love for this phenomenal book, the Bible.

Randy Petersen

"The New Testament is the best book that the world has ever known or will know."
CHARLES DICKENS

"It is impossible to mentally or socially enslave a Bible-reading people."
HORACE GREELEY

"Hold fast to the Bible as the sheet-anchor of your liberties; write its precepts in your hearts and practice them in your lives. To the influence of this book we are indebted for all the progress made in true civilization, and to this we must look as our guide in the future."
ULYSSES S. GRANT

"This great book is the best gift God has given to man. . . . [Without] it we could not know right from wrong."
ABRAHAM LINCOLN

"The Bible is worth all the other books that have ever been printed."
PATRICK HENRY

"The greatest source of material for motion pictures is the Bible, and almost any chapter in the Bible would serve as a basic idea for a motion picture."
CECIL B. DeMILLE

"Most people are bothered by those passages in Scripture which they cannot understand; but as for me, I always noticed that the passages in Scripture which trouble me most are those which I do understand."
MARK TWAIN

"I did not go through the Book. The Book went through me."
A. W. TOZER

"The Bible was never intended to be a book for scholars and specialists only. From the very beginning it was intended to be everybody's book, and that is what it continues to be."
F. F. BRUCE

"Nobody ever outgrows Scripture; the book widens and deepens with our years."
CHARLES SPURGEON

"It is not possible to exhaust the mind of the Scriptures. It is a well that has no bottom."
JOHN CHRYSOSTOM

"The devil can cite Scripture for his purpose."
SHAKESPEARE, *THE MERCHANT OF VENICE*

PART 1:

stuff you probably know

1A
start-up

(GENESIS – 1 SAMUEL)

QUIZ 1A—1

1. With what verse does the Bible begin?
a. In the beginning was the Word, and the Word was with God, and the Word was God.
b. In the beginning God created the heavens and the earth. *Gen 1:1*
c. This is the beginning of the beginning, where all things begin.
d. Once upon a time, there was this garden.

2. Who said, "Let there be light"? *Gen 1:3*
a. Adam
b. The serpent
c. God
d. General Electric

3. After God put in six full days of creating, what did he do on the seventh day?
a. He rested.
b. He created human beings.
c. He created woman.
d. He watched a ball game on TV.

4. Whom did God create in his own image?
a. People
b. The serpent
c. Jesus
d. George Burns

5. Who said it? "Let us make people in our image, to be like ourselves. They will be masters over all life—the fish in the sea, the birds in the sky, and all the livestock, wild animals, and small animals" (Gen. 1:26).
a. The angels of heaven
b. The beasts of Eden
c. God
d. Aliens

6. Eden was:
   a. The third child of Adam and Eve
   b. The garden in which Adam and Eve lived
   c. The name of the serpent who tempted Adam and Eve
   d. The brand name of the apple Adam and Eve ate

7. What did the serpent urge Eve to do?
   a. Untie its tail
   b. Feed it the forbidden fruit
   c. Eat the fruit of the tree of the knowledge of good and evil
   d. Leave Adam

8. Who said it? "The woman you put here with me— she gave me some fruit from the tree, and I ate it" (Gen. 3:12, NIV).
   a. Adam
   b. The serpent
   c. The false prophet
   d. Balaam's donkey

9. To whom did God say, "You will crawl on your belly and . . . eat dust" (NIV)?
   a. Adam
   b. Cain
   c. The serpent
   d. The freshman class of Eden High

10. While Adam and Eve were raising Cain, they were able to raise another son, too. What was his name?
   a. Frank
   b. Abraham
   c. Ananias
   d. Abel

11. After Cain and Abel offered sacrifices to God, Cain did something to his brother. What?
   a. Stole his sacrifice
   b. Killed him

c. Sent him away

d. Told him he was adopted

**12. Who said it? "Am I my brother's keeper?"
(Gen. 4:9, NIV).**

a. Adam

b. Cain

c. Simon Peter

d. Martha

**13. To whom was it said? "Go into the boat with all your
family, for among all the people of the earth, I consider
you alone to be righteous" (Gen. 7:1).**

a. Abraham

b. Noah

c. Shem

d. Curly

14. What was the ark that Noah built?

a. A box that held the holy objects of God

b. A boat that held animals

c. An altar that held offerings to God

d. A skyscraper that touched the heavens

15. Why did God tell Noah to build an ark?

a. People needed to be reminded of God's presence.

b. There was going to be a major flood.

c. Noah was unemployed at the time and bored silly.

d. He meant to say, "Build a *park.*"

**16. If the Weather Channel were around in Noah's day, it
would have reported forty straight days of what?**

a. Calm

b. Rain

c. Blizzard conditions

d. Free cable

17. What sign did God give as a promise he would never again destroy the world with a flood?
   a. Thunder
   b. The olive tree
   c. A rainbow
   d. All of the above

18. In the area of Babel (BABB-ul), people built something that displeased God. What was it?
   a. A box that held the holy objects of God
   b. A boat that held animals
   c. An altar that held offerings to false gods
   d. A skyscraper that touched the heavens

19. Abraham moved with his family to the Promised Land. Why?
   a. God told him to.
   b. The farmland was better there.
   c. They were captured and carried there by Egyptian slave traders.
   d. To play for the local lacrosse team.

20. Canaan (KAY-nun) was:
   a. Abraham's daughter
   b. The name of the Egyptian pharaoh in Abraham's time
   c. The land Abraham moved to
   d. The name of Abraham's pet camel

AMAZING FACTS

The forbidden fruit in the Garden of Eden was probably not an apple. The Bible never says it was. But tradition has it so ingrained that men still have an "Adam's apple" stuck (as it were) in their throats.

YOU SAW IT HERE FIRST

Tattoo

After Cain murdered Abel, God sentenced him to wander the earth, but he put a mark on him so people wouldn't kill him (Gen. 4:15).

Animal Welfare

Old Testament Law had provisions to care for overburdened animals. If you saw the donkey of your enemy struggling under a heavy load, you were supposed to help (Exod. 23:5).

BIBLE BOOKS, PART 1

The whole thing starts in Genesis
With Adam, Noah, Abe, and Joe.
Then Moses leads the Exodus
When Pharaoh lets the people go.
The reading of Leviticus
Is labored, legal, long, and slow.
And then the next book dishes us
More Numbers than we need to know.
But love gives us a little kiss
In the nomy that's called Deutero.

CRAZY ADS

Product
Malicious Apples
   After one bite, you'll know everything's changed.

Billboard
(in region near Babel)
   Future Home of Tower High-Rise. "Reaching the Heavens."

Book
Your Move by **Abram**
   Relocating when you're not sure where you're going

Magazine Cover
Animal Fancy
• Coping When You're Cooped Up
• O Captain, My Captain: A Revealing Look at the Man Who Runs This Ship
• Two by Two: Compatibility Tests for You and Your New Mate
• Seventeen Seasickness Solutions
• In Memorial: The Unicorns That Didn't Make It

Dumb Jokes

Q: Where is baseball in the Bible?
A: "In the big-inning, God created . . ."

Q: What did Adam call the 365 days after his wife was created?
A: New Eve's Year

Q: Why did Adam and Eve become mathematicians?
A: God told them to be fruitful and multiply.

Q: Why did Abel feel neglected?
A: His parents were raising Cain.

Q: Why couldn't Cain please his parents?
A: He just wasn't Abel.

Q: What did Noah say to the people who mocked him?
A: You're all wet!

Q: What did Noah have to learn before he began building?
A: Ark-itecture

Q: How did Noah get the horses to gallop toward the ark?
A: With rains

HIDDEN NOAH

The following nonsense paragraph hides twelve words or names having to do with Noah. Can you find them? (Note: Words and names are strung between the words of the story.)

Flo O'Hara insisted, "I can't bear keeping a secret. I crave news from anywhere. I mean, I'm also the town fool. I've branched out now, so it's amazing what I hear." A rather flighty person, she made no attempt to weigh the consequences. She, like a train, bowled over anyone trying to shush amazing news she had. People considered Flo odd.

The words and names you're looking for:

Animals	Ham
Ararat	Olive branch
Ark	Rain
Dove	Rainbow
Eight	Raven
Flood	Shem

QUIZ 1A—2

1. **To whom was it said? "Is anything too hard for the Lord? About a year from now, just as I told you, I will return, and Sarah will have a son" (Gen. 18:14).**
   a. Noah
   b. Abraham
   c. Naomi
   d. The stork

2. **Jacob and Esau were:**
   a. Twin sons of Rebekah
   b. Twin mountains where Abraham buried Sarah
   c. Twin gems on the high priest's breastplate
   d. Pop stars in the late sixties

3. **Born a few seconds before his brother, Esau had the special rights of the firstborn child, called the "birthright." What did he trade his birthright for?**
   a. Wisdom
   b. A wife
   c. His father's blessing
   d. A bowl of stew

4. **Jacob tricked his blind father into giving him the blessing of the firstborn child. How did he do this?**
   a. He asked for the blessing at night.
   b. He used goatskin to make his arms seem as hairy as Esau's.
   c. He strapped on pillows so he would seem as fat as Esau.
   d. He told his father that Esau had traded him the birthright.

5. **When Esau learned that Jacob had stolen their father's blessing, how did he feel?**
   a. He didn't care.
   b. He wouldn't speak for three days.
   c. He wanted to kill Jacob.
   d. Still hairy.

6. **In a dream, Jacob saw "the angels of God going up and down." Where were these angels?**
   a. On a bright cloud in the night sky
   b. On a stairway to heaven
   c. Around the throne of God
   d. Roller-blading on a half pipe

7. **What piece of clothing did Jacob give his favorite son Joseph?**
   a. A linen ephod
   b. A silver breastplate
   c. A multicolored coat
   d. Socks he had just invented

8. **Pharaoh was so impressed by Joseph's interpretation of his dream that he:**
   a. Released Joseph from prison
   b. Gave him some jewelry
   c. Made him second-in-command in the country
   d. All of the above

9. **Moses' mother sent her baby on a little voyage. What was his means of transportation?**
   a. Camel caravan
   b. Water jug
   c. Basket made of reeds
   d. Greyhound

10. **Who found the baby Moses floating in the water and adopted him as her own child?**
    a. Moses' sister
    b. Pharaoh's daughter

c. Cleopatra

d. None of the above

11. **Which of the following was *not* one of the ten plagues?**

a. Frogs

b. Sharks

c. Flies

d. Gnats

12. **The final plague on Egypt was the most deadly. What was it?**

a. The death of Pharaoh

b. The death of all firstborn sons in Egypt

c. The death of all livestock owned by the Egyptians

d. All of the above

13. **When the Israelites got hungry in the desert, what food did God send from heaven?**

a. Bread, which they called manna

b. Fruit, which they called pomegrana

c. Meat, which they called kosher

d. Apple strudel, which they called pie in the sky

14. **How long did the Israelites wander in the wilderness after escaping from Egypt?**

a. Forty days and forty nights

b. Forty years

c. Seven years of tribulation

d. Until Moses' son Atlas grew old enough to make maps

15. **What major event in Israelite history occurred at Mount Sinai?**

a. God gave them the Law.

b. Moses died.

c. Abraham sacrificed Isaac.

d. Aaron set the worldwide record in downhill skiing.

16. According to the Ten Commandments (KJV), what are you supposed to do with your father and mother?
    a. Love them.
    b. Honor them.
    c. Do everything they say.
    d. Hug them twice a day.

17. What was the golden calf made of?
    a. Bronze candlesticks of the tabernacle
    b. Silver chalices people had stolen from Egypt
    c. Golden jewelry the people wore
    d. Beef

18. Which of the following is *not* one of the Ten Commandments?
    a. Do not testify falsely against your neighbor.
    b. Remember to observe the Sabbath day.
    c. Do not strike your brother in retaliation.
    d. Do not worship any other gods besides me.

19. What did God write his laws on?
    a. Parchments
    b. Stone tablets
    c. The holy ground of Sinai
    d. Legal pads

20. How did God lead the Israelites through the wilderness?
    a. By the Law he gave at Sinai
    b. Each night he told Moses where to lead them the next day.
    c. A pillar of cloud by day, a pillar of fire by night
    d. Bread crumbs

AMAZING FACTS

The word *manna* is Hebrew for "What is it?"

YOU SAW IT HERE FIRST

Nose Ring
You think Generation X invented nose rings? Try Generation Y2KBC. Abraham's servant paid for his stay in Rebekah's home by giving her a gold nose ring and two bracelets (Gen. 24:22).

Love Story
"Rachel was lovely in form, and beautiful. Jacob was in love with Rachel." In fact, he offered to work seven years for her father in order to win her hand in marriage. When the father tricked Jacob into marrying Rachel's sister, Jacob had to work another seven years to get the woman he loved.

BRAIN STUFF
Getting confused about the order of those Old Testament patriarchs—Abraham, Isaac, Jacob, and Joseph? Remember: They're in alphabetical order.

WHAT'S THE SAME?
(What do these things have in common?)
• The sea the Israelites crossed
• The cord Rahab hung outside her window
• Sins
• Esau

ANSWER: All of these things are red.

CRAZY ADS

Video Game
Digger
Keep digging wells, but don't let the bad guys take them over.

Product
Hunty More Red Stew
Only costs one birthright

Service
Seven-Up Dating Services
Because getting the wrong spouse can be costly. Ask about our seven-year guarantee.

Product
Sleepfast Pills
So you stop having dreams that annoy your brothers

Service
Caravan Employment
Only twenty pieces of silver get you started on a career in an exotic location.

WEB SITE
www.joseph.org
Grain supplies in the Mideast. In time of famine, order online and your grain will be waiting for you. Our prime minister instituted a brilliant system of preparation, so we have the grain others want. Avoid embarrassing security checks. Order now.

Dumb Jokes
Q: Which of Jacob's sons could be identified the fastest by his genes?
A: Levi

Q: What did Joseph think of being thrown into a hole in the ground by his brothers?
A: It was the pits.

Q: What did Joseph say when Pharaoh's cup-bearer forgot all about him in prison?
A: "'E-gypt me!"

Q: Why didn't Pharaoh stop swimming when the plagues started?
A: He was in de Nile.

Q: While Aaron was making the golden idol at the base of Mount Sinai, where did he eat?
A: At the calf-eteria

Q: How did Moses react when he saw the golden calf Aaron had made?
A: He had a cow.

Q: How did Pharaoh feel when God put skin lesions on all the Egyptians?
A: He was boiling mad.

MINI-QUIZ: FAMOUS FIRSTS

1. Joseph was not invited to the first birthday party mentioned in Scripture, but a couple of his friends were. Whose birthday was it?

2. He certainly didn't live in a "dry" community, but it's still a bit surprising that he was the first person to get drunk in the Bible. Who was it?

3. The first dream mentioned in Scripture came to Abimelech (uh-BIM-uh-lek), a Canaanite king, warning him to release a woman from his harem. Which woman?

4. The first land purchase was the cave of Machpelah (mak-PEEL-uh), bought by a man as a burial place for his wife. Who was the buyer?

5. Plying her trade as the first shepherdess in Scripture, she landed a man who was on the lam. Who was she?

QUIZ 1A—3

1. **Who said it? "Look, I'm dying of starvation! . . . What good is my birthright to me now?" (Gen. 25:32).**
   a. Abel
   b. Esau
   c. Lazarus
   d. Balaam's donkey

2. **Which of the following were enemies of the Israelites?**
   a. The Trilobites
   b. The Moabites
   c. The Mosquitobites
   d. The Etruscans

3. **Jacob's sons eventually became the tribes of Israel. How many sons did he have?**
   a. Two
   b. Ten
   c. Twelve
   d. Five and a half, if you count Sheldon

4. **Potiphar (POT-ih-far) was:**
   a. The herb Joseph used to fake his death
   b. The country Joseph ran to after his brothers threatened him
   c. The Egyptian who bought Joseph as a slave
   d. The wife Joseph found in Philistia

5. **What happened after the Israelites marched around Jericho thirteen times?**
   a. They marched a fourteenth time.
   b. Jericho's walls fell down.
   c. The army was too dizzy to go on.
   d. Joshua built an altar to the Lord.

6. **Which of the following was *not* one of the judges of Israel?**
   a. Deborah
   b. Samson
   c. Hezekiah
   d. Jephthah

7. **Which of the following *was* one of the judges of Israel?**
   a. Elijah
   b. Rehoboam
   c. Shamgar
   d. Flip

8. **What weapons did Gideon's soldiers take into battle?**
   a. Bows and arrows, and daggers, but no spears
   b. Swords and shields, for hand-to-hand combat
   c. Catapults and boulders
   d. Pitchers, trumpets, and torches

9. **Moses saw something strange in the desert. What was it?**
   a. A bush was burning, but didn't burn up.
   b. A ram was caught in a thicket.
   c. The sky turned black at midday.
   d. A Starbucks coffee shop

10. **Which of the following groups were judges of Israel?**
    a. Tola, Jair, and Jephthah
    b. Aaron, Abner, and Ahithophel
    c. Ephraim, Joab, and Josiah
    d. Tinker, Evers, and Chance

11. **Who were Naomi's daughters-in-law?**
    a. Sally and Oprah
    b. Ruth and Orpah
    c. Bea and Opie
    d. Mary and Martha

12. To whom was it said? "There are still too many [soldiers]! Bring them down to the spring, and I will sort out who will go with you and who will not" (Judges 7:4).

    a. Moses

    b. Gideon

    c. The Moabite commander

    d. Colin Powell

13. Why was Moses' mother afraid that he would die?

    a. He had a disease that only Egyptians had the cure for.

    b. The Egyptians were killing all the Israelite baby boys.

    c. The king's sister wanted the baby for her own.

    d. She was very worried about the Y2KBC bug.

14. Who said it? "Don't ask me to leave you and turn back. I will go wherever you go and live wherever you live. Your people will be my people, and your God will be my God."

    a. Joseph

    b. Miriam

    c. Ruth

    d. Scarlett O'Hara

15. Hannah made a vow to the Lord. If he gave her a child, she would:

    a. Give it right back

    b. Never drink again

    c. Knit coats for all the orphans of Israel

    d. Write a book of the Bible

16. What was the relation of Eli to Samuel?

    a. Eli was Samuel's rebellious son.

    b. Eli was the priest who raised Samuel.

    c. Eli was the prophet who warned Samuel not to trust outward appearances.

    d. Eli was Samuel's evil twin.

17. Who said it? "Speak, for your servant is listening" (1 Sam. 3:10, NIV).
  a. Adam
  b. Moses
  c. Samson
  d. Samuel

18. Why did Samuel wake Eli up in the middle of the night?
  a. He had to go to the bathroom.
  b. He heard a voice calling him.
  c. The house was on fire.
  d. They had forgotten their bedtime prayers.

19. What was Moses' main message to Pharaoh?
  a. God will destroy your kingdom in forty days.
  b. Let my people go!
  c. Give the people straw to make bricks.
  d. Time-and-a-half and paid holidays, or we're going on strike!

20. God gave Joshua the strategy for defeating the walled city of Jericho. What was it?
  a. Surround it, so no supplies could get in
  b. Build a siege ramp and march over the walls
  c. Offer a gift and have Jericho open its gates
  d. March around the city every day for a week

AMAZING FACTS

The Book of Ruth is a great love story, but it doesn't once use the word *love*.

YOU SAW IT HERE FIRST

T-Shirts with Religious Slogans

Well, they weren't exactly T-shirts, but ancient Israelites would write parts of God's law along a fringe they attached to the hems of their garments so they'd be wearing the Word of God—just like Christian teenagers today (Num. 15:38-39).

Drumsticks

Lots of eaters love to claim the drumstick on a chicken or turkey. For them it's a special treat. The same sort of thing appears in the Old Testament. When bringing their sacrificial animal to offer the Lord, the Israelites were told to give the "right thigh" to the priest as a gift (Lev. 7:32).

BIBLE BOOKS, PART 2

> *Joshua, Judges, Ruth—it says*
> *In my Bible's Table of Contents.*
> *And it's true that mighty Joshua has*
> *A lot of positive talents.*
> *And the Moabite widow with Boaz*
> *Might deserve some critical comments,*
> *But her loyalty earns her a lot of applause*
> *While excelling in home economics.*
> *If you really dig for the truth*
> *Brave Joshua mustn't judge Ruth.*
> *When you read the whole book without fudging*
> *It's the Judges who really need judging!*

CRAZY ADS

Product
Bulrush Baby Powder

So you can a–Nile-ate diaper rash whether you're a princess or a lowly slave

Video Game
Mortal Krossing

Cross the Red Sea before Pharaoh's army catches you. Close the sea and watch them drown.

Product
Abracadabra Brand Magic Wand

Throw it down—it becomes a hissing snake. Grab it by its tail— it's a rod again. Amaze all your friends in Pharaoh's court.

Book

Moses Supposes

Tell-all biography by Aaron and Miriam. Moses seems so sure of himself, but he's not!

Product

Dr. Joshua's Comfort Sandals

For those long walks around walled cities

Product

Eli's Night Light

For when your youngsters hear voices in the dark

Magazine

Sports Illuminated

Focus on . . . SAMSON

• How He Keeps Driving Those Phillies Crazy
• Highlights of the Foxtail Fire
• What Those Riddles Really Mean
• Jawbone Jive
• And Our Experts Predict Eventual De-Feet: He'll Die of Fallen Arches

Dumb Jokes

Q: Why didn't the Israelites believe it when their leader told them how to defeat Jericho?

A: They thought he was Joshing.

Q: How did the Israelites feel after seven days of marching around Jericho?

A: Week

Q: What kind of luggage did Delilah take on her honeymoon?

A: Samsonite

Q: Why was Boaz so tough on his workers when his wife took a vacation?

A: He was Ruthless.

Q: Which Israelite leader was an orphan?
A: Joshua, the son of Nun (none—get it?)

Q: What happened to Samson's strength?
A: It vanished into thin hair.

HIDDEN GENESIS PEOPLE

The names of twenty people from the Book of Genesis are hidden in the following nonsense story. Can you find them? (Note: Names are strung between the words of the story; see below for a list of the names you're looking for)

After a while a human craves authority, so the very day he left the tsar, a human—a belligerent Ninja—cobbled and pieced together a machine in his lab and had a masterpiece. "It is a—a coffeemaker. N-no, a h-hotplate," he stuttered as he added multicolored beans—crimson, green, ochre. "It was," he remarked, "a pale vision of bliss, a charming sigh, a garden of delight. Ironic, ain't it? After all this, I'm eons away from completion." Taking a draught of his latest drink, he added, "That sure be Kahlua."

Names you're looking for:

Abel	Isaac
Adam	Issachar
Asher	Jacob
Cain	Laban
Dan	Leah
Enoch	Levi
Esau	Noah
Eve	Rebekah
Gad	Sarah
Hagar	Simeon

TV LISTINGS

Drama
Homicide
> Two brothers. One farms. One tends. One kills.
> Guest starring Cain, Abel

Sitcom
The Odd Couple
> Two Brothers. One hunts, the other cooks. Watch what happens
> when the hunter comes home hungry, ready to trade anything
> for a good meal.

Soap Opera
The Edge of Sight
> Mother schemes to give her younger son the inheritance, tricking
> her blind husband into choosing the wrong boy.

MOVIE OF THE WEEK
"Ordinary" Joe
> Favored by his father but hated by his brothers, he became a slave
> in a foreign land. Jailed for a crime he didn't commit, he became
> leader of a nation in crisis! Jealousy! Passion! Revenge! Reunion!

Sitcom
Mr. E
> Starring Balaam and his talking donkey. Tonight: he's "touched
> by an angel." Della Reese costars.

1B
kings & things

(1 SAMUEL—ESTHER)

QUIZ 1B—1

1. Who was the first king of Israel?
a. Samuel
b. Saul
c. David
d. Henry I

2. Who was the second king of Israel?
a. Saul
b. David
c. Jonathan
d. Richard II

3. Who was the third king of Israel?
a. David
b. Absalom
c. Solomon
d. George III

4. Who poured oil on David's head to anoint him as king of Israel?
a. Saul
b. Moses
c. Samuel
d. Wesson

5. What did David do to try to soothe King Saul's nerves?
a. Gave him a massage
b. Played the harp
c. Killed Philistines
d. Let him win at chess

6. What giant did David kill?
a. Saul
b. Absalom
c. Goliath
d. Andre

7. **What weapon did David use to slay the giant?**
   a. A bow and arrow his father had given him
   b. A slingshot
   c. The holy sword of King Saul
   d. Vicious sheep

8. **As Saul chased David through the desert caverns of Judea, David had opportunities to creep up on Saul and kill him. Why didn't he?**
   a. Because Saul was still God's anointed king.
   b. Because he didn't think he could escape from Saul's soldiers.
   c. Because he wasn't carrying any weapons.
   d. Because Saul hypnotized him.

9. **What city did David establish as his capital?**
   a. Samaria
   b. Jericho
   c. Jerusalem
   d. Davidia

10. **What prince became a dear friend of David?**
    a. Abinadab, son of Samuel
    b. Jonathan, son of Saul
    c. Rehoboam, son of Solomon
    d. Albert, in a can

11. **On the way up the hill to Jerusalem, David "danced before the Lord with all his might" (2 Sam. 6:14-15). What was the occasion?**
    a. The dedication of the temple
    b. The ark of the covenant was being brought to Jerusalem
    c. The final defeat of the Philistines
    d. Assyrian Bandstand

12. **David committed adultery with the wife of Uriah. What was her name?**
    a. Michal
    b. Abigail

c. Bathsheba

d. The queen of Sheba

13. How did David have Uriah killed?

a. He commanded his archers to shoot Uriah in the back.

b. He had Uriah "accidentally" fall into a pit at a building project.

c. He sent Uriah to the army's front lines and had the army pull back.

d. He made him teach sixth-grade Sunday school.

14. What prophet challenged David about his adultery and murder?

a. Elijah

b. Samuel

c. Nathan

d. Hosea

15. Who "wore a bronze helmet and a coat of mail that weighed 125 pounds" (1 Sam. 17:5)?

a. Saul

b. David

c. Goliath

d. Jesse Ventura

16. What son of David launched a rebellion against him?

a. Solomon

b. Absalom

c. Maccabee

d. Judas

17. Which king of Israel built the first temple?

a. David

b. Solomon

c. Nehemiah

d. Trump

18. **In a dream God offered Solomon anything he wanted. What did Solomon ask for?**
    a. More wealth than anyone on earth
    b. Wisdom
    c. Compassion for those less fortunate
    d. Ice cream

19. **What monarch came to visit Solomon "to test him with hard questions" (1 Kings 10:1)?**
    a. King Hiram of Tyre
    b. The queen of Sheba
    c. Pharaoh Rameses of Egypt
    d. Old King Cole

20. **A government official named Jeroboam (JAIR-uh-BOH-uhm) led a revolt against Solomon's son Rehoboam (REE-uh-BOH-uhm), splitting the kingdom in two. The northern kingdom became known as Israel. The southern kingdom took the name of its major tribe. What was it?**
    a. Benjamin
    b. Negev
    c. Judah
    d. Tahiti

YOU SAW IT HERE FIRST

Music Therapy

Modern psychologists are studying ways to use music and other arts to improve mental health. David was doing this in 1000 B.C., as he played the harp to soothe King Saul's manic depression (1 Sam. 16:14-23). Of course, Saul once flung a spear at David in midsong, but that's just an occupational hazard.

Overpriced Water

Do you have a hard time paying a buck or two for bottled water? Consider what a drink of water cost David. Once in battle against the Philistines he mused, "Oh, how I would love some of that good water from the well in Bethlehem, the one by the gate." Three of his best soldiers broke through enemy lines to get him that drink. He was so moved, he refused to drink it (1 Chron. 11:17-19).

BIBLE BOOKS, PART 3

Samuel, Kings, Chronicles
Most have one book, but these three have two.
If you're jamming on things historical
These six books will give you a few.
From Hannah to Cyrus, I reckon,
They'll give you the best and the worst.
But I keep looking all through the second
For things I can find in the first.

CRAZY ADS

Want Ad
Wanted: King for a small tribal Mideast country. Benefits include taxes, army, possible harem. No experience necessary. Height a plus. Send resume to Samuel, Town Hall, Ramah.

Video Game
Konk Kong
You get five pebbles. Sling them at the giant's head. If you win, Goliath dieth. But watch out for that big sword.

Dumb Jokes

Q: What was David's anthem as he faced Goliath?
A: "Of Thee I Sling"

Q: Why didn't the Israelite soldiers want to fight Goliath?
A: It was a tall order.

Q: How could people tell that David was a shepherd when he fled from Saul?
A: He went on the lam.

HIDDEN DAVID

The following nonsense story hides twelve names or words associated with David. Can you find them? (Note: Words and names are strung between the words of the story.)

Entering his room, I challenged my travel agent, Al J., essentially to find me a place to stay in the Philippines. "Ling's Hotel offers good lodging and access to cabs," Al omnisciently replied, "but every beggar keeps alms for himself. I once took Mrs. J. on a Thanksgiving trip there, but she got sunburned, so she wasn't in a thankful mood. Now when she takes a bath, she bastes her back with an ointment. And those cooks sure know how to char pork. The artful stew they serve is better than the kind that Esau loved."

Here's what you're looking for:

Absalom	Jonathan
Anoint	Michal
Bathsheba	Nathan
Harp	Psalms
Heart	Saul
Jesse	Slingshot

QUIZ 1B—2

1. **King Ahab married a foreign queen who led Israel into the worship of false gods. What was her name?**
   a. Delilah
   b. Jezebel
   c. Esther
   d. Elvira

2. **What prophet confronted King Ahab about the idolatry of the nation?**
   a. Nathan
   b. Elijah
   c. Isaiah
   d. Madonna

3. Which of the following were kings of Israel?
  a. Micaiah, Obadiah, Ehud
  b. Jotham, Zebedee, Tishri
  c. Omri, Ahab, Jehu
  d. Kaline, Cash, Freehan

4. What weather condition did Elijah predict?
  a. Rain
  b. Drought
  c. Snow
  d. Hurricane Jezebel

5. Where was this said? "How long are you going to waver between two opinions? If the Lord is God, follow him! But if Baal is God, then follow him! . . . The god who answers by setting fire to the wood is the true God!" (1 Kings 18:21-24).
  a. Mount Ararat
  b. Mount Sinai
  c. Mount Carmel
  d. Mount Everest

6. Which of the following were kings of Judah?
  a. Jehoshaphat, Hezekiah, Josiah
  b. Haggai, Ezra, Pul
  c. John Paul, George, Ringo
  d. Pekah, Ben-hadad, Thutmose

7. Who had 700 wives and 300 concubines?
  a. David
  b. Solomon
  c. Herod
  d. Whoever he was, he was very tired

8. What false god was worshiped in Israel during the reign of Ahab and other kings?
  a. Zeus
  b. Baal

c. Isis

d. Mammon

9. **Who did Ahab call "Israel's troublemaker" (1 Kings 18:16–17)?**
   a. Obadiah
   b. Elijah
   c. John the Baptist
   d. Jezebel

10. **What was the outcome of the contest on Mount Carmel?**
    a. Elijah's sacrifice was consumed by fire.
    b. Only the prophets of Baal succeeded in calling fire from heaven.
    c. Both sacrifices were consumed.
    d. The contest was rained out.

11. **What prophet did Elijah anoint as his successor?**
    a. Elijah Jr.
    b. Elisha
    c. Eli
    d. E-I-E-I-O

12. **How did Elijah feel after his great victory over the prophets of Baal?**
    a. So pumped that he stormed the palace and confronted the queen.
    b. Afraid that the queen would hunt him down and kill him.
    c. Concerned that the prophets of Baal would be depressed.
    d. So self-righteous that God blinded him temporarily.

13. **What happened the last time Elisha saw Elijah?**
    a. Elijah, on his deathbed, asked Elisha for an oath of loyalty.
    b. A chariot of fire appeared, and a whirlwind took Elijah to heaven.
    c. Elijah was being publicly burned to death by Jezebel's soldiers.
    d. Elisha asked Elijah to change his name because people were getting confused.

14. **What piece of clothing did Elisha pick up as he began to carry on Elijah's ministry?**
    a. Jezebel's royal robe
    b. Day-Glo bell-bottoms
    c. Elijah's cloak
    d. Elijah's leather belt

15. **Naaman was an Aramean commander who came to Elisha for healing. What was his problem?**
    a. Headaches
    b. Leprosy
    c. Blindness
    d. Low self-esteem

16. **How did Naaman react when asked to wash seven times in the Jordan River?**
    a. He was angry that Elisha didn't greet him personally.
    b. He was glad that he wouldn't have to do anything difficult.
    c. He was embarrassed by his unclean appearance.
    d. He was afraid he would make the river unclean for others.

17. **How much did Elisha charge Naaman to heal him?**
    a. Nothing
    b. One silver piece
    c. The chariot he came in
    d. Just the minimal HMO fee

18. **King Nebuchadnezzar (NEB-yu-cud-NEZ-er) took Judah captive around 586 B.C. What nation did he lead?**
    a. Egypt
    b. Babylon
    c. Macedonia
    d. Nebuchadnezzaria

19. **King Joash took the throne at age seven and pleased the Lord with his leadership. What structure did he seek to rebuild during his reign?**
    a. His palace

b. The temple

c. The health spa

d. The water tunnel

20. In 2 Kings 17, what reasons are given for the downfall of the northern kingdom of Israel?

a. High taxes, a weak army

b. Idol worship, rejection of God

c. Unwise alliances with neighboring nations

d. Not enough peanut butter

YOU SAW IT HERE FIRST

Mouth-to-Mouth Resuscitation

The prophet Elisha brought a little boy back from the dead with a process amazingly like modern mouth-to-mouth (2 Kings 4:34).

Master of Disguise

It was a plan worthy of *Mission: Impossible.* King Ahab heard a prophecy that he would die in the battle he was about to fight against the Arameans, so he dressed as a common soldier. His ally, King Jehoshaphat, wore his royal robes into battle—and went unscathed. "An Aramean soldier, however, randomly shot an arrow at the Israelite troops, and the arrow hit the king of Israel [Ahab] between the joints of his armor." Badly wounded, he apparently bled to death, fulfilling the grim prophecy (1 Kings 22).

Piggy Bank

Well, it certainly wasn't shaped like a pig, but it was the same idea—a container for money with a slot in the top. King Joash was collecting money for temple repairs, but apparently the priests were skimming some funds for their own needs. So the high priest "bored a hole in the lid of a large chest." Then people would drop their contributions in it. When it became full, the court secretary and high priest would open it.

BRAIN STUFF

Of course you're getting Jeroboam and Rehoboam mixed up. They're the two guys who split Solomon's kingdom, north and south. Well, first note that, north to south, they're in alphabetical order—Jeroboam in the north, Rehoboam in the south. But to get the history, think of Jeroboam as the onetime government official who was *jeering* at *royal* Rehoboam. Reho was Solomon's son, and he wanted everyone to know how royal he was. That's what made Jeroboam jeer.

CRAZY ADS

Product
Raven Brand Lunch Meats
When your famished, just sit by a brook and enjoy our tasty treats. We deliver. One out of fifty prophets agree—it's a life-saving meal.

Product
Baal-Beater Lighter Fluid
When your altar just won't draw fires

Dumb Jokes

Q: What happened to all the idolaters after Elijah defeated the prophets on Mount Carmel?
A: They Baaled.

QUIZ 1B–3

1. **The Assyrian army threatened the southern kingdom of Judah, besieging Jerusalem during the reign of what king?**
   a. David
   b. Rehoboam
   c. Hezekiah
   d. Elvis

2. **Who challenged the prophets of Baal to a sacrificing duel on Mount Carmel?**
   a. David
   b. Elijah
   c. Isaiah
   d. Balaam

3. **During the rebuilding of Jerusalem's wall, builders worked with one hand while they did what with the other?**
   a. Helped one another
   b. Held a weapon
   c. Steadied themselves
   d. Applauded

4. **What did King Hezekiah do when he learn he had a terminal illness?**
   a. He hired the best doctors in Judea.
   b. He sent to Egypt for medical experts.
   c. He began taking herbal treatments prescribed in the books of Moses.
   d. He prayed.

5. **To whom was it said? "I chose you to lead my people Israel when you were just a shepherd boy, tending your sheep out in the pasture. . . . Now I will make your name famous throughout the earth!" (1 Chron. 17:7-8).**
   a. Abraham
   b. David
   c. Elijah
   d. Frank Perdue

6. **According to 1 Chronicles 28:3, why didn't God let David build the temple?**
   a. Because he had committed adultery with the wife of Uriah.
   b. Because he was a warrior and had shed much blood.
   c. Because he had failed calculus.
   d. Because since Absalom's revolt he had lost the love of the people.

7. **What had a total wingspan of 30 feet (2 Chron. 3:11)?**
   a. The golden angels in the temple's Most Holy Place
   b. The creatures Ezekiel saw within the wheels
   c. All the birds aboard Noah's ark
   d. The pterodactyl that wouldn't fit in Noah's ark

8. **What was the occasion? "The trumpeters and singers performed together in unison to praise and give thanks to the Lord. . . . At that moment a cloud filled the Temple of the Lord. The priests could not continue their work because the glorious presence of the Lord filled the Temple of God" (2 Chron. 5:7, 13-14).**
   a. David had conquered the Philistines.
   b. The ark of the covenant was brought to the temple.
   c. Elijah had defeated the prophets of Baal at Mount Carmel.
   d. The early church met its financial goals.

9. **Who was described as "a hairy man, [who] wore a leather belt around his waist" (2 Kings 1:8)?**
   a. Adam
   b. Cain
   c. Elijah
   d. Fabio

10. **Who built a new palace for an Egyptian wife because he couldn't let a foreigner live in David's palace, which he considered holy (2 Chron. 8:11)?**
    a. Samuel
    b. Solomon
    c. Mordecai
    d. Malachi

11. **During which king's reign did Israelite ships sail to the land of Ophir and bring back seventeen tons of gold (2 Chron. 8:18)?**
    a. Saul
    b. Ahab

c. Midas

d. Solomon

12. **Who said it? "Everything I heard in my country about your achievements and wisdom is true! . . . Truly I had not heard the half of it! Your wisdom is far greater than what I was told" (2 Chron. 9:5-6).**

  a. Rahab

  b. Boaz

  c. The queen of Sheba

  d. Alex Trebek

13. **Who was "richer and wiser than any other king in all the earth" (2 Chron. 9:22)?**

  a. David

  b. Solomon

  c. Herod

  d. Larry King

14. **What king of Judah had the fewest letters in his name? (In English, not Hebrew.)**

  a. Og

  b. Asa

  c. Saul

  d. Tiglath-Pileser

15. **Who decreed this? "The Lord, the God of heaven, has given me all the kingdoms of the earth. He has appointed me to build him a Temple at Jerusalem in the land of Judah. All of you who are his people may return to Jerusalem in Judah to rebuild this Temple" (Ezra 1:2-3).**

  a. Pharaoh of Egypt

  b. King Cyrus of Persia

  c. King Solomon

  d. David Ben-Gurion

16. **Whom does the Bible describe as "a scribe, well-versed in the law of Moses. . . . He came up to Jerusalem from Babylon and the king gave him everything he asked for"?**
    a. Ezra
    b. Caleb
    c. Nathanael
    d. Hawthorne

17. **Mordecai had a cousin named Hadassah, who was brought into the king's harem. What was Hadassah's Persian name?**
    a. Shadrach
    b. Vashti
    c. Esther
    d. Hadassah II

18. **Which of the following were Old Testament prophets?**
    a. Jephthah, Othniel, and Shamgar
    b. Elisha, Obadiah, and Balaam
    c. Joshua, Zerubbabel, and Nehemiah
    d. James, John, and Andrew

19. **In which of the following books would you find stories of David?**
    a. 1 Chronicles
    b. 1 Samuel
    c. 2 Samuel
    d. All of the above

20. **What scribe read God's Word to the people at the Water Gate?**
    a. Nicodemus
    b. Nixon
    c. Ezra
    d. Asaph

YOU SAW IT HERE FIRST

Cranking up the Music

Long before rock and roll, the Israelites were cranking up their music. David instructed the Levites to play "on harps and lyres and cymbals, to raise loud sounds of joy" (1 Chron. 15:16, NRSV). Sounds like a modern rock band with guitars and drum sets. The ark of the covenant was brought into Jerusalem "with the sounding of rams' horns and trumpets, and of cymbals, and the playing of lyres and harps" (1 Chron. 15:28). Scripture mentions several other worship services where the music and shouting got "loud" (2 Chron. 15:14), even "very loud" (2 Chron. 20:19).

BIBLE BOOKS, PART 3

A writer, a butler, a queen—
It sounds like a silly joke,
But the writer made a scene
That encouraged the common folk.
The butler became a builder,
Though he often met with frustration.
The queen's husband nearly killed her,
But she bravely saved her nation.
A clerk, a cup-bearer, a queen—
It sounds like a tiny tongue twister
Until you see that I mean
Ezra, Nehemiah, and Esther.

CRAZY ADS

Video Game
Nehemiah

Build the wall around the city before your enemies knock it down. One button does the building, while the other fights off your foes.

Dumb Jokes

Q: Why didn't Haman use the gallows he had built to execute Mordecai?

A: He couldn't get the hang of it.

Q: What did it say on the card the king sent Nehemiah?

A: Many happy returns

TV LISTINGS

Sitcom

Who's the Boss?

Crazy antics as Saul chases David through the desert—both claiming to be king!

Movie

Twister

Elijah thumbs a ride to heaven on a category 7 whirlwind, leaving Elisha to check his coat.

1C
the write stuff

(JOB—MALACHI)

QUIZ 1C—1

1. **Who said it? "I have been going back and forth across the earth, watching everything that's going on" (Job 1:7).**
   a. Satan
   b. Gabriel
   c. Paul
   d. Boeing

2. **According to Satan, why did Job honor God?**
   a. Because God had protected him and made him rich.
   b. Because he was foolish.
   c. Because his parents had taught him to.
   d. Because his three friends made him.

3. **What physical affliction did Job suffer from?**
   a. A terrible cough
   b. Boils
   c. Blindness
   d. Tennis elbow

4. **Which of the following statements best sums up what Job's friends told him?**
   a. The sun'll come up tomorrow. Bet your bottom dollar.
   b. You must have done something to deserve all this.
   c. Try to learn something from these disasters.
   d. We feel your pain.

5. **A fourth friend, Elihu, shows up later in the book of Job. What does he have to say?**
   a. God can do whatever he wants.
   b. Job, maybe you can fool these guys with your innocent act—not me.
   c. My friends, quit talking and help this guy!
   d. Boils! Yuck!

6. **What happened at the end of Job's story?**
   a. Satan was locked up for a thousand years.

    b. Job's goods were restored by twice as much, and he got ten more children.

    c. Job's friends left in disgust, except Elihu, who became king.

    d. They woke up.

7. **Which of the following people are *not* mentioned in Psalm 1:1 as "blessed" or joyous people?**

    a. Those who do not follow the advice of the wicked

    b. Those who do not dance with immoral people

    c. Those who do not stand around with sinners

    d. Those who do not join in with scoffers

8. **Who wrote the most psalms?**

    a. Twila Paris

    b. Moses

    c. Solomon

    d. David

9. **Finish this verse: "When I consider your heavens, the work of your fingers, the moon and the stars, which you have set in place . . ." (Psalm 8:3-4, NIV)**

    a. I marvel at your glorious handiwork.

    b. I realize my own insignificance.

    c. what is man that you are mindful of him?

    d. wow, like that's really, really awesome.

10. **According to Psalm 14:1, who say in their hearts, "There is no God"?**

    a. The wicked

    b. Fools

    c. Those who use arrogant words

    d. Atheists

11. **According to Psalm 19:1, what "tell of the glory of God . . . display his marvelous craftsmanship"?**

    a. The people who serve the Lord

    b. The heavens and the skies

c. Events of our lives

d. Best-sellers from Tyndale House Publishers

12. **Finish this verse: "My God, my God! Why have you . . ." (Psalm 22:1)**
    a. created this world of wonder?
    b. forsaken me?
    c. delivered me from my enemies when I have displeased you?
    d. created me?

13. **Finish this verse: "The Lord is my shepherd . . ." (Psalm 23:1, KJV)**
    a. and I am his sheep.
    b. he leads me through life.
    c. I shall not want.
    d. who beats me with his rod and staff.

14. **According to Psalm 23:2, where does the Lord "let me rest"?**
    a. In his holy house (temple)
    b. In heavenly places forever
    c. In green meadows (pastures)
    d. In my La-Z-Boy recliner

15. **In Psalm 23, David says he "fears no evil" even though he's walking where?**
    a. Up a high, rocky cliff
    b. Through the dark valley of death
    c. On rocks across a swift stream
    d. Across the interstate

16. **According to Psalm 23 (KJV), what will "follow me all the days of my life"?**
    a. Your loving footsteps
    b. The dark deeds of my past
    c. Goodness and mercy
    d. The CIA

17. Finish this verse: "Be still . . ." (Psalm 46:10, NIV)
   a. my child, be still.
   b. because the Lord is nigh to you.
   c. and know that I am God.
   d. because your fidgeting is driving me crazy!

18. Finish this verse: "Wash me, and I will be . . ." (Psalm 51:7)
   a. faithful all of my days.
   b. clean and upright in your presence, O Lord.
   c. whiter than snow.
   d. out of the dryer in twenty minutes.

19. According to Psalm 90:1 (NIV), who has been "our dwelling place throughout all generations"?
   a. The Lord
   b. Adam and Eve
   c. Abraham
   d. Mother Earth

20. Finish this verse: "Enter his gates with thanksgiving . . ." (Psalm 100:4)
   a. but leave with a heavy heart.
   b. go into his courts with praise.
   c. for he has done many marvelous deeds.
   d. but wipe your feet first.

AMAZING FACTS

The word *God* or *Lord* appears in every book of the Bible except Esther and Song of Songs.

The phrase "the skin of my teeth" originally appeared in the Bible (Job. 19:20).

BIBLE BOOKS, PART 4

All the Bible books are wise
But some are "Books of Wisdom."

A closer study of these five
Enlarges readers' vision.
Job depicts a righteous guy
Who faces great affliction.
The psalms sing out and magnify
The Lord (despite some friction).
Proverbs shows the laws of life
To bright young men and women.
Ecclesiastes seems to whine
And offer criticism.
And Song of Songs looks through the eyes
Of lovers who are smitten.
All the Bible books are wise,
But these win recognition
For cutting through our normal lives
And finding precious wisdom.

QUIZ 1C–2

1. **The first word of Psalms is also the first word of Jesus' Sermon on the Mount in Matthew 5 (NIV). What is that word?**
   a. The
   b. Blessed
   c. Hallelujah
   d. Sing

2. **According to Psalm 103:12, how far has God removed our sins from us?**
   a. As far as the islands of the sea
   b. As far as the east is from the west
   c. Out of sight and out of mind
   d. A couple miles

3. **Finish this verse: "This is the day the Lord has made . . ." (Psalm 118:24)**
   a. this is his holy Sabbath.
   b. so take care to do righteousness while the sun shines.

c. we will rejoice and be glad in it.

d. tomorrow may be another story.

4. **Fill in the blanks: "Your word is a _____ for my feet and a _____ for my path" (Psalm 119:105).**

   a. wing, smoothing

   b. lamp, light

   c. comfort, delight

   d. bunion, rest stop

5. **According to Psalm 119:11, where has the psalmist hidden God's Word?**

   a. Under a bushel

   b. In his heart

   c. Where the wicked cannot go

   d. Under his bed

6. **In Psalm 122:1, the psalmist rejoices when they say what to him?**

   a. "Let us go to the house of the Lord."

   b. "Well done, good and faithful servant."

   c. "The Lord has done great things for us."

   d. "Let's eat."

7. **Finish this verse: "Search me, O God, and know my heart . . ." (Psalm 139:23)**

   a. test me and know my thoughts.

   b. lead me in the way everlasting.

   c. forgive the sin that resides there.

   d. but don't look too closely.

8. **Which of the following is *not* mentioned in Psalms 149 or 150 as a way to praise the Lord?**

   a. Dancing

   b. Preaching

   c. Tambourine

   d. Cymbals

9. **Who wrote most of the Proverbs?**
   a. David
   b. Solomon
   c. The Preacher
   d. Confucius

10. **How many chapters are there in the book of Psalms?**
    a. 7
    b. 50
    c. 150
    d. One very long one

11. **Finish this verse: "Fear of the Lord is . . ." (Prov. 1:7)**
    a. essential to pleasing him.
    b. the beginning of knowledge.
    c. the downfall of the timid.
    d. not required anymore.

12. **Finish this verse: "Trust in the Lord with all your heart . . ." (Prov. 3:5)**
    a. do not depend on your own understanding.
    b. give him the firstfruits of all your goods.
    c. and love him with heart, soul, and mind.
    d. because no one else around here can be counted on.

13. **According to Proverbs 15:1, what does a gentle answer turn away?**
    a. Suspicion or fear
    b. Anger or wrath
    c. Trouble or evil
    d. Attention

14. **Which of the following is *not* listed as an activity of "the virtuous wife" in Proverbs 31?**
    a. She gets up before dawn to prepare breakfast.
    b. She goes out to inspect a field and buys it.

c. She teaches her children from her own knowledge.

d. She watches for bargains.

15. **Finish this verse: The husband of the "virtuous wife" says about her, "There are many virtuous and capable women in the world . . ." (Prov. 31:29)**

    a. and you are truly one of them.

    b. but you surpass them all.

    c. and I could have married any one of them.

    d. so why do you keep comparing yourself to them?

16. **The Lord asked, "Whom should I send as a messenger to my people? Who will go for us?" How did Isaiah respond?**

    a. "I don't speak well, but my brother does. Send him."

    b. "Lord, I'll go. Send me!"

    c. He remained silent in God's presence.

    d. He ran like crazy away from there.

17. **Isaiah saw angels with six wings in the temple—with two wings they covered their faces, with two they covered their feet. What did they do with the other two wings?**

    a. They applauded.

    b. They reached out to Isaiah.

    c. They fanned the flame on the altar.

    d. They flew.

18. **Isaiah prophesied about the birth of a child who would be named Immanuel (Isa. 7:14). What does that mean?**

    a. Go to my people.

    b. God is with us.

    c. Prophet of God

    d. Let us pray.

19. **Fill in the blank: Isaiah prophesied about the birth of Christ: "For unto us a _____ is born; unto us a _____ is given" (Isa. 9:6, KJV).**
    a. Saviour/Lord
    b. child/son
    c. hope/gift
    d. love/life

20. **Which of the following is *not* one of the royal titles Isaiah mentions in his messianic prophecy (Isa. 9:6)?**
    a. Wonderful Counselor
    b. Prince of Peace
    c. Ruler of All Flesh
    d. Everlasting Father

AMAZING FACTS

The word *Selah* appears often between verses in the book of Psalms. No one knows what it means. Take a guess. You might be right.

BIBLE BOOKS, PART 5

A prophet sees a prophecy and speaks of now and then;
He'll challenge things and chastise kings with actions, voice, and pen.
Isaiah knew a servant who would be the slaughtered Lamb,
And Jeremiah cared and cried about his wayward land
(His Lamentations show frustration few can understand).
Ezekiel played the renegade with dry bones reuniting,
And Daniel braved the lions' cave and read a wall with writing.
Hosea wed a girl who said "I do" but wasn't honest,
And Joel foretold that young and old would share the Spirit's promise.
Amos aimed his famous blame at folks who wouldn't heed him.
Obadiah warned of dire consequence for Edom.
Jonah trekked the wrong direction, then just wept and whaled.
Micah penned that Bethlehem would be a fertile field.
Nahum cheered that the Assyrians soon would see defeat.
Habakkuk drew the letters huge so everyone could read.
Zephaniah kept on trying to inspire repentance.

Haggai chilled the straggling builders of the temple entrance.
Zechariah said to Zion, "See, your king will come."
Malachi foresaw Elijah forerunning the One.
Prophets used their office to get people to look higher;
Some would trash their harmful actions, disarm their desire.
Others praised the Maker's ways or warned of judgment's fire,
And some would just proclaim their trust in God's promised Messiah.

CRAZY ADS

Product
Baruch 7.0 Word Processing Software
Next time the king burns your scroll, just print out a new one.

Dumb Jokes

Q: Which prophet was most likely to wear contact lenses?
A: "Eyes"-aiah (Isaiah)

Q: Which book of the Bible is simplest to read?
A: "Easy"-kiel (Ezekiel)

MINI-QUIZ: SEASONS

"There is a time for everything, a season for every activity under heaven," says Ecclesiastes 3, which lists several pairs of contrasting activities. See if you can match them up.

1. A time to be born . . .	a. and a time to laugh
2. A time to plant . . .	b. and a time to gather stones
3. A time to kill . . .	c. and a time to die
4. A time to tear down . . .	d. and a time to throw away
5. A time to cry . . .	e. and a time to hate
6. A time to grieve . . .	f. and a time to heal
7. A time to scatter stones . . .	g. and a time to turn away
8. A time to embrace . . .	h. and a time for peace
9. A time to search . . .	i. and a time to speak up
10. A time to keep . . .	j. and a time to mend
11. A time to tear . . .	k. and a time to dance

12. A time to be quiet . . .   l. and a time to rebuild
13. A time to love . . .   m. and a time to lose
14. A time for war . . .   n. and a time to harvest

QUIZ 1C-3

1. In Isaiah 53, the Servant is compared to what animal?
   a. A strong ox
   b. A majestic stallion
   c. A sacrificial lamb
   d. A soaring eagle

2. Fill in the blanks: "He was despised and _____, a man of _____, acquainted with bitterest grief" (Isaiah 53:3).
   a. spat upon/bitterness
   b. rejected/sorrows
   c. humiliated/no repute
   d. hated/mystery

3. Who is known as the "weeping prophet"?
   a. Elisha
   b. Jeremiah
   c. Malachi
   d. Tammy Faye

4. Who said it? "My God sent his angel to shut the lions' mouths so that they would not hurt me."
   a. David
   b. Darius
   c. Daniel
   d. Siegfried and Roy

5. The book of Lamentations laments the fall of what city?
   a. Jerusalem
   b. Damascus
   c. Alexandria
   d. Jericho

6. **Fill in the blanks: "Because of the Lord's great love we are not _____, for his _____ never fail. They are new every _____; great is your _____"** (Lam. 3:22-23, NIV).
   a. evil, plans, prayer, love
   b. defeated, purposes, time, mystery
   c. consumed, compassions, morning, faithfulness
   d. Methodists, church bulletins, week, Sunday school

7. **Who won a high government position after interpreting a dream for the king?**
   a. David, and later Jonathan
   b. Joseph, and later Daniel
   c. Esther, and later Joseph
   d. Daniel, and later Freud

8. **To whom was it said? "Get up and go to the great city of Nineveh! Announce my judgment against it because I have seen how wicked its people are."**
   a. Elijah
   b. Jonah
   c. Nahum
   d. Peter

9. **King Belshazzar threw a big party, and all the guests saw a hand. What was the hand doing?**
   a. Clapping
   b. Pointing at the king
   c. Writing on the wall
   d. Giving a big thumbs-up

10. **Fill in the blank: "They sow the wind and reap the _____"** (Hos. 8:7, NIV).
    a. consequences
    b. whirlwind
    c. harvest of wickedness
    d. breeze

11. **What prophet was a fish dinner?**
    a. Micaiah
    b. Obadiah
    c. Jonah
    d. Micah

12. **The Lord told Habakkuk to write down his answer in what way (Hab. 2:2)?**
    a. In tiny letters so that only the priests could read it
    b. In large, clear letters so even the messenger could read it and tell everyone
    c. In a hidden language that the Lord would reveal to him
    d. Double-spaced, with footnotes

13. **To whom was it said? "My wise man and enchanters have tried to read this writing on the wall, but they cannot. I am told that you can give interpretations and solve difficult problems."**
    a. Joseph
    b. Daniel
    c. Malachi
    d. Einstein

14. **Haggai prophesied to the Jews in the time of Zerubbabel and the high priest Jeshua. What structure did he challenge them to rebuild?**
    a. The king's palace
    b. The temple
    c. The altar at Samaria
    d. Zerubbabel's nameplate

15. **Which minor prophets of the Old Testament have the fewest letters in their name?**
    a. Gad and Asa
    b. Amos and Joel
    c. Nahum and Micah
    d. Zechariah and Zephaniah

16. **Finish this verse: "Why are you living in luxurious houses while . . ." (Hag. 1:3)**
    a. there are poor people in the land?
    b. you play idle songs on your six-stringed lyres?
    c. my house lies in ruins?
    d. mortgage rates are sky-high?

17. **Zechariah prophesied about the coming of a king—righteous and victorious, but humble (Zech. 9:9). Upon what was the king riding?**
    a. A great white horse
    b. The shoulders of his devoted followers
    c. A donkey
    d. A tank

18. **Fill in the blank: "Strike down the shepherd, and the sheep will be _____" (Zech. 13:7).**
    a. set free
    b. stronger
    c. scattered
    d. mutton

19. **Malachi prophesies about someone who will "prepare the way" before the Lord (Mal. 3:1). What does Malachi call this person?**
    a. The Enforcer
    b. A messenger
    c. Savior
    d. John

20. **What is the last book of the Old Testament?**
    a. Zephaniah
    b. Micah
    c. Malachi
    d. Revelation

YOU SAW IT HERE FIRST

Secretary
Baruch faithfully recorded the message from God that Jeremiah dictated (Jer. 36:4).

UFO
Ezekiel saw a vision of some creatures flying in a contraption of wheels within wheels. Check out the description for yourself in Ezekiel 1.

BRAIN STUFF
How to remember Daniel's fired-up friends, Shadrach, Meshach, and Abednego? Try this nighttime ritual: Shake the bed, Make the bed, and To bed we go. Sure it's stupid, but you'll remember!

CRAZY ADS

Tabloid
Nineveh Inquirer
Man Swallowed by Whale
• No Fish Story: This Jewish Prophet Was Hurled to shore and He's Here to Preach.
• Massive Repentance: King Himself Says to Pay Heed.
• Jonah: "No comment."

Dumb Jokes
Q: What's the prophets' national anthem?
A: "Hosea, can you see. . . ."

Q: Which prophet couldn't sing?
A: Na-HUM

Q: Which prophet was most likely to be a fireman?
A: "Hose"-ea (Hosea)

Q: On what road would you find Daniel's lions' den?
A: Mane Street

TV LISTINGS

Movie of the Week
The Lion King

Simba meets a nice prophet in the den, decides to keep his friends from eating him.

Soap Opera
Mad about You

Hosea's crazy for Gomer, but she keeps him guessing. This week: He sends her flowers, but she thinks they're from Baal.

1D
good news
(MATTHEW – JOHN)

QUIZ 1D—1

1. **Who was Jesus' mother?**
   a. Mary
   b. Mary Magdalene
   c. Martha
   d. Elizabeth

2. **What gifts did the three magi give to Jesus?**
   a. Gold, frankincense, and myrrh
   b. Milk and honey
   c. Swaddling clothes
   d. Embroidered booties

3. **What angel appeared to both Zechariah and Mary?**
   a. Gabriel
   b. Daniel
   c. Raphael
   d. Roma

4. **What did the angel Gabriel announce to Mary?**
   a. Joseph was leaving her.
   b. Her cousin Elizabeth was saying bad things about her.
   c. God would deliver Israel from the Romans.
   d. She would become pregnant with Jesus.

5. **How long did the angel say Jesus' kingdom would last?**
   a. One thousand years
   b. A time and times and half a time
   c. Thirty-three years
   d. It would never end.

6. **Fill in the blank: "For nothing is _____ with God"
   (Luke 1:37).**
   a. wrong
   b. impossible
   c. unexpected
   d. everything

7. **Who "leaped" when Elizabeth met with Mary?**
   a. Elizabeth
   b. Mary
   c. Elizabeth's baby, in her womb
   d. Elizabeth's flea circus

8. **Who sent out a decree that a census should be taken of the entire Roman world?**
   a. King Herod
   b. Caesar Augustus
   c. Nero
   d. AT&T

9. **Where did Joseph and Mary have to go to register for the census?**
   a. Jerusalem
   b. Nazareth
   c. Bethlehem
   d. High school

10. **What kind of crib was baby Jesus laid in?**
    a. A kitchen cabinet
    b. A bread basket
    c. A manger, used to feed cattle
    d. Fisher-Price

11. **Who told the shepherds in the nearby fields about the birth of Jesus?**
    a. Joseph's relatives
    b. Wise men
    c. An angel of the Lord
    d. Their sheep

12. **According to John 1:1, what was in the beginning and was with God?**
    a. The heaven and earth
    b. Wisdom

    c. The Word

    d. The Big Bang

13. Fill in the blank: "The Word became _____ and made his dwelling among us" (John 1:14, NIV).
    a. light
    b. love
    c. flesh
    d. imperfect

14. Where did John the Baptist baptize people?
    a. The Sea of Galilee
    b. The Jordan River
    c. His bathtub
    d. The Dead Sea

15. When Jesus was baptized, the Spirit of God descended upon him like what?
    a. A mighty wind
    b. A dove
    c. A leaf
    d. A roller coaster

16. How long did Jesus fast in the desert?
    a. Forty days and forty nights
    b. Thirty days and forty nights
    c. Three days and three nights
    d. Six days, then he rested

17. Who tempted Jesus in the desert?
    a. Peter, James, and John
    b. The devil
    c. Pontius Pilate
    d. Judas Iscariot

18. **Who was pictured on the Roman coin shown to Jesus by the Pharisees?**
    a. Jesus
    b. Caesar
    c. Darius
    d. Alan Greenspan

19. **Which commandment did Jesus say was the greatest?**
    a. Do not kill.
    b. Have no other gods before me.
    c. Love the Lord your God with all your heart, all your soul, and all your mind.
    d. Don't use your toaster in the bathtub.

20. **Which commandment is "equally important"?**
    a. Do not commit adultery.
    b. Make no graven image.
    c. Love your neighbor as yourself.
    d. Do not cut off mattress tags.

BIBLE BOOKS, PART 6

Matthew marked the prophecies so fellow Jews would know.
Mark looked at the actions, showing Jesus on the go.
Luke joined Jesus' parables with carefully checked facts.
John discussed the meaning of the Savior's saving acts.
In Acts we witness the exploding witness to the world—
Banners made by Matthew, Mark, Luke, John are now unfurled.

CRAZY ADS

Video game
Follow That Star
    Hitch your camel to a star and follow it through the maze to Bethlehem. Just watch out for that double-crossing king.

Product
Bapt-O-Bar
The candy bar with honey and *real* locusts

Dumb Jokes

Q: Why did the shepherds go to see baby Jesus?
A: They herd the news.

Q: How did the sheep feel about seeing baby Jesus?
A: Baa-shful.

QUIZ 1D—2

1. Which of the following actions did the devil *not* ask Jesus to do during the temptation?
a. Turn stones to bread
b. Curse God and die
c. Throw himself from the high point of the temple
d. Kneel down and worship the devil

2. Finish this phrase: "For many are called, but few are _____" (Matt. 22:14).
a. loved
b. worthy
c. chosen
d. answering their phones

3. How many disciples did Jesus call during his ministry (Matt. 10:1-4)?
a. Four
b. Twelve
c. Eighty
d. Three thousand

4. The wise builder builds his house on what ground?
a. Rock
b. Sand

c. Loam

d. Swamp

5. **Where should a lamp be put so those who come in can see the light?**

   a. On a stand

   b. Under a bushel

   c. On one's head

   d. In our hearts

6. **Moses and Elijah make an appearance in the Gospels. What are they doing?**

   a. Preaching to the crowds near Galilee

   b. Appearing to Pilate in a dream

   c. Talking with Jesus on the Mount of Transfiguration

   d. Shooting hoops

7. **What does a good shepherd do for his sheep?**

   a. Lays down his life

   b. Finds them safe pasture

   c. Cleans their wool

   d. Teaches them how to be sheep

8. **What three friends of Jesus lived (and/or died) in the town of Bethany?**

   a. Mary, Martha, and Lazarus

   b. Peter, James, and John

   c. Nathanael and his parents

   d. Saul, David, and Solomon

9. **According to the Gospel of Matthew, what two brothers were the first disciples called by Jesus?**

   a. Simon Peter and Andrew

   b. James and Judas

   c. John and Levi

   d. Cain and Abel

10. **What was the occupation of the first four disciples Matthew mentions?**
    a. Tax collectors
    b. Carpenters
    c. Fishermen
    d. Insurance salesmen

11. **According to Matthew 5:6 (NIV), what will happen to those who hunger and thirst for righteousness?**
    a. They will be honored by the high court of heaven.
    b. They will inherit the earth.
    c. They will be filled.
    d. They will get extra dessert.

12. **Fill in the blank: Jesus said, "You are the ____ of the world" (Matt. 5:14).**
    a. light
    b. salvation
    c. lambs
    d. greatest people

13. **If someone strikes you on the right cheek, what should you do?**
    a. Hit the person back, on the cheek.
    b. "Turn the other cheek" so you might get hit again.
    c. Let the person hit you again, then wallop him.
    d. Sue.

14. **According to Matthew 5:44, how are we to treat our enemies?**
    a. Ignore them and they'll go away.
    b. Don't give them cause to hurt us.
    c. Love them and pray for them.
    d. Don't get mad; get even.

15. **Where did Jesus say we should store up treasures?**
    a. In the temple
    b. In heaven

c. In the secret places of the earth

d. Mutual funds

16. Who, in all his splendor, was not dressed as well as the lilies of the field?

a. Noah

b. Solomon

c. Herod

d. Liberace

17. If you notice a speck of sawdust in your brother's eye, what is the first thing you should do?

a. Call a doctor

b. Call a carpenter

c. Pray

d. Remove the plank from your own eye

18. Why did the disciples awaken Jesus when they were in their boat on the lake?

a. They had lost their way.

b. They were afraid they would drown in the storm.

c. They were worried that they didn't have enough bread.

d. He was sleepwalking.

19. To whom was it said? "Stand up, take your mat, and go on home" (Matt. 9:6).

a. A paralyzed man healed by Jesus

b. A beggar the Pharisees were trying to move from the temple

c. Levi, at his tax collection booth

d. Richard Simmons

20. What was Matthew's occupation before he became a disciple of Jesus?

a. Fisherman

b. Pharisee

c. Tax collector

d. Actuary

AMAZING FACTS

The term "a wolf in sheep's clothing" comes from Scripture—from Jesus' warning about false prophets (Matt. 7:15).

CRAZY ADS

Business
Heavenly Treasures Financial Planning Services
   Get a better yield when you yield to God

BUSINESS
Lily's Clothing Boutique (formerly Solomon's)
   We don't work hard, but our clothes still look great!

PRODUCT
Angel Wings Bungee Cords
   When you just can't resist jumping off a temple

Dumb Jokes

Q: What did Jesus eat after being in the desert forty days and forty nights?
A: Fast food.

Q: Why did Jesus perform his first miracle at the wedding in Cana?
A: His mother wined about it.

MINI-QUIZ: SEEDS AND SOILS

Jesus told a parable of a farmer sowing seed into different types of soil (Matt. 13). Match the soil with the outcome.

1. Footpath   a. Produced a bigger crop than was planted.
2. Shallow soil   b. Plants sprang up, then wilted.
3. Among thorns   c. Birds ate the seeds.
4. Fertile soil   d. Plants were choked.

QUIZ 1D—3

1. **The devil told Jesus to turn what inanimate objects into what food?**
   a. Stones into bread
   b. Wood to figs
   c. Mud to meat
   d. Peas to grapes

2. **Fill in the blanks: "Look, I am sending you out as _____ among _____" (Matt. 10:16).**
   a. doves, vultures
   b. sheep, wolves
   c. lions, giants
   d. clippers, hedges

3. **Finish this phrase: "For my yoke is easy and my burden is _____" (Matt. 11:30, NIV).**
   a. smaller than a man's fist
   b. deep
   c. light
   d. for all people of this land

4. **A merchant found something of such great value that he sold everything he had and bought it. What did he buy?**
   a. A boat
   b. A wineskin
   c. A pearl
   d. A home entertainment center

5. **How much food did Jesus need to feed a crowd of five thousand?**
   a. Seven cartloads of fruit and bread
   b. Twelve baskets of bread and wine
   c. Five loaves and two fishes
   d. 144 cartons of Captain Crunch cereal

6. **Which disciple tried to join Jesus in his walk on the water?**
   a. Lazarus
   b. Peter
   c. Bartholomew
   d. Jacques Cousteau

7. **To whom was it said? "Upon this rock I will build my church" (Matt. 16:18).**
   a. Simon Peter
   b. Jesus
   c. Pontius Pilate
   d. Larry Norman

8. **What did Jesus tell his disciples they should "take up" to follow him (Matt. 16:24, NIV)?**
   a. Their sins
   b. Their hypocritical attitudes
   c. Their cross
   d. Shuffleboard

9. **Fill in the blank: "Unless you turn from your sins and become as _____, you will never get into the Kingdom of Heaven" (Matt. 18:3).**
   a. angels
   b. my followers
   c. little children
   d. Pharisees

10. **If a shepherd owns one hundred sheep and one of them wanders off, what will he do?**
    a. Let it go
    b. Leave the ninety-nine to look for the one
    c. Ask the ninety-nine to lead him to the one
    d. Run away

11. **Jesus said it was harder for a rich person to enter the kingdom of God than for a camel to do what?**
    a. Go a week without water
    b. Go through the eye of a needle
    c. Shed its hump
    d. Water-ski

12. **Finish this verse: "Many who are first will be last, and the last will be . . ." (Matt. 19:30, NRSV)**
    a. supreme.
    b. farther ahead.
    c. first.
    d. hungry.

13. **What will happen to those who exalt themselves?**
    a. They will be humbled.
    b. They will be judged on the last day.
    c. They will get a lucrative book contract.
    d. They will lose their friends one by one.

14. **Finish this verse: "Whoever is the least among you is . . ." (Luke 9:48)**
    a. lucky.
    b. the greatest.
    c. not worthy of me.
    d. least among me.

15. **Who said he was the light of the world (John 8:12)?**
    a. John the Baptist
    b. Jesus
    c. King Herod
    d. Thomas Edison

16. **Finish this verse: "You will know the truth . . ." (John 8:32)**
    a. and your lives will be richer for it.
    b. and your enemies will know only falsehood.

c. and the truth will set you free.

d. of your errors and repent of your sin.

17. Where did Jesus attend a wedding feast with his mother?

a. In Jerusalem

b. In Herod's palace

c. In Cana in Galilee

d. At the Nazareth fire hall

18. Finish this phrase: Seek and you will _____ (Luke 11:9, NIV).

a. be fulfilled

b. gain new friends

c. find

d. seek

19. In the parable of the Good Samaritan, who passed by the beaten man?

a. A priest and a Levite

b. A Samaritan and a swindler

c. John the Baptist and Jesus

d. A rabbi, a priest, and a Baptist preacher

20. Which of the following did the Samaritan *not* do for the beaten man?

a. Bind his wounds

b. Take him to an inn

c. Hunt down the robbers

d. Pay for the man's lodging

YOU SAW IT HERE FIRST

Traveling Salesman

No joke! The Good Samaritan was probably a traveling salesman. He *was* traveling on a dangerous road by himself, and he had his own donkey. He also carried cash (he paid the innkeeper two silver coins) and said he'd be coming back that way again (Luke 10:30–37).

CRAZY ADS

Newspaper Headline
Man Mugged on Jerusalem Journey
Good Samaritan Saves His Life
"Never Saw Him," Say Priest, Levite

Business
Daze Inn
If you get beaten to a bloody pulp on your travels—tell your
local Samaritan to bring you here! Medical services available.

Web Site
www.sheepfind.com
Locate that missing lamb electronically! Why leave the ninety-
nine? Go online and see where your ram has rambled!

QUIZ 1D–4

1. **What was the occasion? "You are my beloved Son,
   and I am fully pleased with you" (Mark 1:11).**
   a. Jesus' birth
   b. Jesus' baptism
   c. Jesus' temptation
   d. Jesus' first preaching at Capernaum

2. **Friends brought a paralyzed man to Jesus, but the house
   was crowded. How did they get him in to see Jesus?**
   a. They bribed the guards.
   b. They called from the hill outside.
   c. They made an opening in the roof and lowered the man
      down.
   d. They yelled "Fire!" so everyone would leave.

3. **What happens to a house divided against itself
   (Mark 3:25, NIV)?**
   a. It cannot stand.
   b. It causes only grief.
   c. It turns on other houses.
   d. It becomes a duplex.

4. **What was the situation? "Teacher, don't you even care that we are going to drown?" (Mark 4:38).**
   a. Peter was trying to walk on water.
   b. The disciples were afraid in a terrible storm.
   c. The Israelites were afraid to cross the Red Sea.
   d. The lame men were afraid to dip themselves in the Pool of Siloam.

5. **Where is a prophet without honor?**
   a. Among other prophets
   b. In the den of iniquity
   c. In his hometown
   d. Philadelphia

6. **How did John the Baptist die?**
   a. King Herod had him beheaded.
   b. He was hanged by the Roman authorities.
   c. He fell on his way up Mount Carmel.
   d. He drowned.

7. **Finish this verse: "What good is it for a man to gain the whole world, yet forfeit . . ." (Mark 8:36, NIV)**
   a. that world to evil.
   b. his soul.
   c. his worldly wealth.
   d. his good name.

8. **What color did Jesus' clothes become during the Transfiguration?**
   a. Scarlet, as if the sin of the world fell on him
   b. Blue, as blue as the sky above
   c. Dazzling white, whiter than anyone in the world could bleach them
   d. Mauve, or more like peach, in a beige sort of khaki

9. In Jesus' teaching, if your eye causes you to sin, what should you do?
a. Gouge it out
b. Close it
c. Blink three times and click your heels
d. Get contacts

10. The Son of Man did not come to be served, but to do what?
a. To preach
b. To serve
c. To be
d. To create the church

11. Finish this verse: "Give to Caesar what is Caesar's and . . ." (Mark 12:17, NIV)
a. give me one-tenth of your goods.
b. to the Pharisees not a penny.
c. to God what is God's.
d. half of what is yours.

12. How much money did Jesus see a poor widow put in the temple treasury?
a. Two small copper coins
b. Her entire fortune, ten talents of gold
c. Twenty pieces of silver
d. None, but she took out $2.73.

13. According to Jesus, why was the widow's gift greater than all the others?
a. She gave with a pure heart.
b. It was all she had.
c. The others just pretended to give.
d. Those coins were collector's items.

14. Jesus predicted that Peter would deny him three times before what event?

a. Before the crucifixion

b. Before the Son of Man returned

c. Before the rooster crowed

d. Before the authorities stopped persecuting his disciples

15. What would a woman sweep every nook and cranny of her house to find?

a. A lost coin

b. A lost sheep

c. The deed to her home

d. Her glasses

16. Foxes have holes and birds of the air have nests, but the Son of Man has what?

a. Only a small room

b. No place to lay his head

c. The company of friends

d. Motel 6

17. A man said he wanted to follow Jesus but had to bury his father first. What was Jesus' reply (Luke 9:60, NIV)?

a. Honor your father, but hurry back here.

b. Bury yourself first in my teaching.

c. Let the dead bury their own dead.

d. He'll wait.

18. What two sisters welcomed Jesus into their house?

a. Mary and Martha

b. Elizabeth and Mary

c. Lydia and Dorcas

d. Laverne and Shirley

19. **What went wrong at the wedding feast, and what did Jesus do about it?**
    a. The groom got nervous, but Jesus comforted him.
    b. There was an unruly Pharisee, but Jesus silenced him with a witty response.
    c. They ran out of wine, so Jesus turned some water into wine.
    d. The DJ kept playing polkas, so Jesus taught everyone to dance.

20. **The rich fool wanted to take life easy—eat, drink and what?**
    a. Sleep
    b. Marry
    c. Be merry
    d. See Mary

CRAZY ADS

Service
H & R Flock Tax Services
    When you have to render to Caesar

Product
Finders Keepers Power Sweepers
    Vacuum action will find your missing coins fast. Let the neighbors rejoice!

Product
Cana Wine
    We save the best for last.

Dumb Jokes

Q: What did John the Baptist say to his executioner?
A: Don't ax me

Q: Why was John the Baptist so upset about being killed?
A: He just lost his head

QUIZ 1D—5

1. **In the Lord's Prayer, what do we ask God to give us?**
   a. Money
   b. Peace
   c. Daily bread
   d. New sneakers

2. **In the Lord's Prayer, where do we ask not to be led?**
   a. Into temptation
   b. Into the valley of the shadow of death
   c. Into forgiveness
   d. Into his will

3. **What was Mary doing while Martha was working and worrying?**
   a. Working and whistling
   b. Sitting at Jesus' feet, listening to him teach
   c. Standing in the backyard gossiping with James and John
   d. Singing

4. **What did Jesus say are "numbered"?**
   a. Our days
   b. The hairs on our heads
   c. Our problems
   d. Our seats in heaven

5. **The youngest son who squandered his inheritance wound up doing what for a living?**
   a. Fishing
   b. Taking care of pigs
   c. Making pots
   d. Flipping burgers

6. **In Jesus' parable, what was the father's reaction to the return of his youngest son?**
   a. He threw a feast.
   b. He gave the boy his finest robe.

c. He killed the fatted calf.

d. All of the above

7. What was the older brother's reaction to his brother's return?

a. He rejoiced that the lost was found.

b. He was glad he'd have someone to boss around again.

c. He was angry and jealous.

d. He ran away from home.

**8. Finish this phrase: "No servant can serve two _____"
(Luke 16:13, NIV).**

a. purposes

b. masters

c. meals at the same time

d. all of the above

9. What friend did Jesus raise from the dead?

a. Mary

b. Martha

c. Lazarus

d. John the Baptist

10. What did Jesus tell Nicodemus he must do in order to see the kingdom of God?

a. Be born again

b. Keep the commandments

c. Sell everything and give to the poor

d. Change his name

11. According to John 3:16, how much did God love the world?

a. Enough to spare it from the working of his wrath

b. So much that he gave his only Son

c. More than the world will ever know

d. A whole lot

12. **What did Jesus offer to the Samaritan woman at the well?**
    a. The truths of God
    b. Living water
    c. Pardon for her immoral life
    d. Gum

13. **Finish this verse: "I am the bread of . . ." (John 6:35)**
    a. contention.
    b. life.
    c. suffering.
    d. healing.

14. **Jesus said, "All right, stone her. But let those who have never sinned throw the first stones!" (John 8:7). What woman was he talking about?**
    a. Mary Magdalene
    b. A woman captured in the act of adultery
    c. The wife of King Herod's brother
    d. He was speaking figuratively of the church.

15. **Who did Jesus call "a liar and the father of lies" (John 8:44)?**
    a. The devil
    b. Caiaphas, the chief priest
    c. Judas Iscariot
    d. The rich young ruler

16. **Who sent word to Jesus that Lazarus was sick?**
    a. John
    b. Mary and Martha
    c. The centurion who found Lazarus along the road
    d. The ER team

17. **How did tiny Zacchaeus manage to see Jesus as he entered Jericho?**
    a. He bought a house along Jesus' route.
    b. He crawled to the front of the line.
    c. He climbed up a tree.
    d. Mirrors

18. **What act did Jesus perform for his disciples to set an example of how they should serve one another?**
    a. He washed their feet.
    b. He cooked some lentil stew.
    c. He carried James on his back halfway to Bethany.
    d. He prayed for them.

19. **Jesus said the Father would send someone else in his name after he was gone. Who?**
    a. Elijah
    b. Peter, the Rock
    c. The Counselor, or Comforter—the Holy Spirit
    d. The Son of Man

20. **If Jesus is the vine, his disciples are what?**
    a. The wine
    b. The branches
    c. The vineyard
    d. Divine

FAQ

Q: Why do some churches say "debts" in the Lord's Prayer and others say "trespasses"?

A: It's basically a difference between two of the earliest translators of the Bible into English—William Tyndale and John Wycliffe. In 1525, Tyndale translated Matthew 6:12 as "forgive us our trespasses." But back in 1380, Wycliffe had used *debts* (or *dettes* in early English). In the late 1500s, other Bible translations followed Wycliffe's lead, as did the popular King James Version (1611), using *debts*. But *The Book of Common Prayer* (1549) went with Tyndale's *trespasses,* and that became standard for the Anglican Church and other churches (like Methodists) that stemmed from them.

CRAZY ADS

Magazine
Home Beautiful
Martha of Bethany
• Being Ready for Unexpected Guests—A Dozen of Them!
• Exciting New Recipes for Lentil Stew
• How to Get Your Lazy Sister to Help
• Brother Laz Says She Makes a Double-Chocolate Cake to Die For—Twice!

Business
Prodigal Bus Lines
    You *can* go home again!

Service
Nicodemus Birth Center
    Once . . . and again!

Dumb Jokes

Q: How did Martha feel about doing all the kitchen work herself?
A: She wasn't merry (Mary).

QUIZ 1D—6: PASSION WEEK

1. **As Jesus rode into Jerusalem, what did the crowd put on the road in front of Jesus?**
    a. Sand
    b. Palm branches
    c. Prayers they had written down
    d. Donkey food

2. **What animal did Jesus ride into Jerusalem?**
    a. A horse
    b. A camel
    c. A donkey
    d. A heifer

3. **What garden did Jesus and his disciples go to after their Passover meal?**
   a. Gethsemane
   b. Eden
   c. Kidron
   d. Bethany

4. **On what occasion was it said? "This is my blood, which seals the covenant between God and his people. It is poured out to forgive the sins of many" (Matt. 26:28).**
   a. The Sermon on the Mount
   b. The Last Supper
   c. Jesus' death on the cross
   d. Jesus' meeting with his disciples after the resurrection

5. **When Mary Magdalene and the other Mary went to look at the tomb, what did they find?**
   a. They couldn't find the tomb.
   b. The stone was rolled back, and the angel of the Lord was sitting there.
   c. The soldiers were asleep and the tomb sealed shut.
   d. An angel chorus was singing God's praises.

6. **What did the crowd shout when Pilate asked them what he should do with Jesus?**
   a. "Release him to us!"
   b. "Listen to his teachings!"
   c. "Make him king! Death to Caesar!"
   d. "Crucify him!"

7. **One of the criminals crucified next to Jesus asked to be remembered when Jesus came into his kingdom. What did Jesus say?**
   a. "Today you will be with me in paradise."
   b. "My kingdom is not of this world."
   c. "Your sins are many, too many to see forgiveness."
   d. "Are you ready to drink the cup of suffering?"

8. **Where did Joseph of Arimathea place Jesus' body?**
   a. In a new tomb carved out of rock
   b. In his own home
   c. In the cool basement of the Roman fortress
   d. In the grave he had just dug in the earth

9. **Finish this verse: "Take it and eat it, for this is my . . ."**
   (Matt. 26:26)
   a. gift to you.
   b. body.
   c. final meal with all of you.
   d. remembrance.

10. **Who denied Jesus before the rooster crowed?**
    a. Judas
    b. Peter
    c. James
    d. Paul

11. **Finish this verse: "Father, forgive these people, because**
    . . ." (Luke 23:34)
    a. they don't know what they are doing.
    b. they are blinded by greed and fear.
    c. it is in your nature to forgive.
    d. they are truly trying to follow you.

12. **Why did Mary Magdalene, Mary the mother of James,**
    and Salome go to Jesus' tomb when the Sabbath was
    over?
    a. To make sure no one had broken in
    b. To anoint the body with spices for burial
    c. Because Jesus had promised to rise from the dead
    d. To bribe the soldiers

13. **What did the risen Jesus show the disciples to convince**
    them that it was really him?
    a. A piece of the cross
    b. His graveclothes

c. His pierced hands and side

d. The coin he had taken from a fish's mouth

14. Which disciple still had doubts that Jesus had risen?

a. Peter

b. Thomas

c. Judas

d. Lazarus

15. When Judas saw that Jesus was condemned, what did he do?

a. He ran away from Judea.

b. He tried to comfort the other disciples.

c. He returned the priests' money and hanged himself.

d. He joined the crowd around the cross.

16. Who was the Roman governor who tried Jesus?

a. Pontius Pilate

b. Herod Agrippa

c. Nero

d. Caiaphas

17. What prearranged signal did Judas use to show the priests which person to arrest?

a. He turned his back to Jesus.

b. He gave Jesus a kiss of greeting.

c. He led all the others away from Jesus.

d. He handed Jesus a cup of vinegar.

18. A sign was placed on Jesus' cross. What did it say?

a. Truly this was the Son of God.

b. Stop and wonder, all you who pass by.

c. This is Jesus, the King of the Jews.

d. Save yourself!

19. Who put Jesus in his own tomb?

a. Zacchaeus

b. Simon Peter

c. Joseph of Arimathea
d. Pontius Pilate

20. To whom was it said? "Put your hand into the wound in my side. Don't be faithless any longer. Believe!" (John 20:27).
a. Thomas
b. Peter
c. John the Baptist
d. Paul

CRAZY ADS

Video Game
Donkey Throng
Dodge the branches people are throwing as you carry the King safely into the city. But watch out for Pharisees as you scoop up the singing stones!

Encounter Group
Skeptics Anonymous
"Is there a problem we can't help you with?" asks Thomas Didymus, our founder.
"I doubt it!"

TV LISTINGS

Movie of the Week
The River Wild
A wild man named John gains a following as he dunks people who repent. This week: A mysterious stranger seeks baptism, and those present hear a voice from heaven.

Drama
ER
Get involved in the lives of the people who come to Jesus for healing. This week, a synagogue ruler, a Roman centurion, and a hemophiliac woman. Will Lazarus pull through?

Soap Opera
The Young and the Restless
Teenage son cashes in his trust fund and lives high on the hog. But when times get tough, will Dad take him back? And what about his hardworking older brother?

1E
church chat
(ACTS—REVELATION)

QUIZ 1E—1

1. Fill in the blanks: "But you will receive _____ when
   the Holy Spirit comes on you; and you will be my
   _____ in Jerusalem, and in all Judea and Samaria, and
   to the _____ of the earth" (Acts 1:8, NIV).
   a. confidence, eyes, nations
   b. power, witnesses, ends
   c. eternal life, holy apostles, far reaches
   d. money, bankers, trust funds

2. What had just happened? "As they were straining their
   eyes to see him, two white-robed men suddenly stood
   there among them. They said, 'Men of Galilee, why are
   you standing here staring at the sky'" (Acts 1:10–11).
   a. Elijah had just ridden his fiery chariot to heaven.
   b. The fire of the Lord's presence had just appeared above the
      apostles.
   c. Jesus had just ascended into heaven.
   d. The helicopter had been invented.

3. "Suddenly there was a sound from heaven like the roaring of a mighty windstorm . . . and it filled the house
   where they were meeting. Then, what looked like flames
   or tongues of fire appeared and settled on each of them"
   (Acts 2:2–3). When did this happen?
   a. When Jesus ascended to heaven
   b. At the day of Pentecost, when the Spirit filled the disciples
   c. When Paul first preached the gospel to the Gentiles
   d. When Matthew forgot to turn off the coffeemaker

4. What was strange about the way Jesus' disciples were
   speaking on the day of Pentecost?
   a. People from different nations understood them in their
      own languages.
   b. They sounded just like Jesus.
   c. No one could understand a word they were saying.
   d. They weren't using any verbs.

5. **About three thousand people became followers of Jesus on what day?**
   a. Pentecost
   b. The day Jesus fed the five thousand
   c. Good Friday
   d. The Day of Atonement

6. **Peter and John met a lame beggar and said they had no money for him. What did they give him instead?**
   a. Advice on his spiritual journey
   b. A cloak
   c. Healing
   d. High-yield Internet stocks

7. **Who said it? "We must obey God rather than human authority" (Acts 5:29).**
   a. Saul, to Ananias
   b. Peter and the apostles
   c. Lydia, to the Philippian jailer
   d. Cornelius, resigning from his Roman army post

8. **Among the seven deacons the apostles chose to help them were Philip, five men you've never heard of, and one other. Who was that other deacon?**
   a. Bartholomew
   b. Stephen
   c. Silas
   d. Paul

9. **Stephen was the first Christian martyr. How did he die?**
   a. He was stoned to death.
   b. He was crucified.
   c. He was sent out into the desert without water.
   d. He was thrown into the arena with lions.

10. **When he saw some water along the side of the road, what did the Ethiopian eunuch suggest to Philip?**
    a. That they stop and drink
    b. That Jesus was the living water
    c. That Philip should baptize him
    d. That they should splash around a bit

11. **What persecutor of the church was stopped by a bright light on the road to Damascus?**
    a. Caiaphas
    b. Saul
    c. Peter
    d. Gamaliel

12. **What is the distinction of Cornelius, a Roman centurion?**
    a. The most honored commander in the Roman army
    b. The last man to see Peter alive
    c. The first Gentile to become a Christian
    d. The only man shorter than Zacchaeus

13. **Who had a vision in which he was commanded to eat nonkosher foods?**
    a. Paul
    b. Peter
    c. Agrippa
    d. Oscar Mayer

14. **Finish this verse: "I am not ashamed of the . . ." (Rom. 1:16, NIV)**
    a. Lord Jesus Christ.
    b. gospel.
    c. church I serve.
    d. scars I bear.

15. According to Romans 3:23, who has sinned?
a. The Gentiles
b. The Jews
c. The Samaritans
d. All of the above

16. What are the "wages of sin" (Rom. 6:23)?
a. Enmity between friends and curses among brothers
b. Eternal separation from all that is good
c. Death
d. About $4.50 an hour, before taxes

17. Who is the author of 1 Corinthians?
a. Timothy
b. Silas
c. Paul
d. Corinth

18. What is "the temple of the Holy Spirit" (1 Cor. 6:19)?
a. Your body
b The temple in Jerusalem
c. The nation of Israel
d. Your forehead

19. Finish this verse: "There are three things that will endure—faith, hope, and love—and the greatest of these is . . ." (1 Cor. 13:13)
a. faith.
b. hope.
c. love.
d. greater than any power on earth.

20. Finish this verse: "Therefore, if anyone is in Christ, he is . . ." (2 Cor. 5:17, NIV)
a. saved, sanctified, and heaven-bound!
b. a new creation; the old has gone, the new has come!
c. free from all pain and worry; joy is his!
d. expected to follow all that Jesus has commanded.

BIBLE BOOKS, PART 8

Romans gives us doctrine: we're not saved by law, but grace.
Both Corinthian letters cover problems we might face
(A special thirteenth chapter eases love into first place).
Galatians deals with law and grace (a shorter draft of Romans);
Ephesians shows us how to be God's church (though we are humans).
Philippians brings joy (though Paul was writing it in prison);
Colossians warns of teachings that don't focus on Christ risen.
Two Thessalonians say rapture's imminent—then isn't.
Then Timothy gets two epistles, even though he's young.
Like Titus, he gets guidance as to keeping churches strong.
Philemon is a postcard begging lenience for a slave,
And Hebrews shows that Christ is far more powerful to save.
(One chapter focuses on faith of heroes bold and brave.)
But James won't take faith lightly; he needs to know it works.
And Peter in two letters tries to help a suff'ring church.
John has one epistle and two postcards all on love.
Then Jude sneaks in a warning of false teachers he knows of.
And finally Revelation—seven letters all in one—
Along with wondrous prophecies of wonders yet to come,
And a final feat on heaven's streets with God's beloved Son.

CRAZY ADS

Web Site
www.pentecost.com
See who's being added to the church every day!

Video Game
Jailbirds
Keep preaching, keeping getting arrested, keep getting out.

QUIZ 1E–2

1. **Barnabas was sent to Tarsus to bring back a man who would become a great missionary (Acts 11:25). Who?**
   a. Mark
   b. Philemon
   c. Saul
   d. Billy Graham

2. **Peter was imprisoned in King Herod's crackdown against the church. Who sprang him from jail?**
   a. Mark and Timothy
   b. Rhoda
   c. An angel
   d. The church's new SWAT team

3. **Some Christians were at Mary's house, praying for Peter, who was in prison. When someone knocked at the door, a servant girl named Rhoda answered. Who was it?**
   a. Rhoda's ex-husband
   b. James and John
   c. Roman soldiers, looking for Peter
   d. Peter

4. **What missionaries did the church of Antioch send out (Acts 13:1-4)?**
   a. Peter and John
   b. Agabus and Andrew
   c. Barnabas and Saul
   d. Silas and Timothy

5. **The people of Lystra thought these two were the gods Zeus and Hermes. Who were they really?**
   a. Jupiter and Mercury
   b. Barnabas and Paul (formerly Saul)
   c. Joseph and Mary
   d. Emperor Nero and Governor Pliny

6. **A missionary named Silas preached in Philippi and other towns. Who was his traveling companion?**
   a. Paul
   b. James
   c. Matthias
   d. His wife, Elizabeth

7. **In Lystra, Paul met a young man who joined his ministry team. Later he wrote letters to this associate. Who was that young man?**
   a. Mark
   b. Luke
   c. Timothy
   d. Thessalonica

8. **Paul and Silas cast a demon out of a slave girl and were thrown in jail for it. Why?**
   a. They cast it into the town's chief magistrate.
   b. The girl's masters were unhappy since they'd been using her possession for profit.
   c. The demon stirred up lies against them.
   d. They were double-parked at the time.

9. **What were Paul and Silas doing in a Philippian jail when an earthquake struck?**
   a. Preaching to the other prisoners
   b. Sleeping
   c. Praying and singing hymns
   d. Digging a tunnel

10. **According to 1 Corinthians 13, what is "patient and kind . . . not jealous or boastful or proud or rude"?**
    a. The Spirit
    b. Faith
    c. The soul of the believer
    d. Love

11. **God loves the person who gives in what way?**
    a. Generously
    b. Cheerfully
    c. Without sin in one's heart
    d. Every Sunday

12. **Which of the following is *not* one of the "fruit of the Spirit" (Gal. 5:22-23)?**
    a. Love
    b. Diligence
    c. Self-control
    d. Patience

13. **Who gets a foothold from our anger (Eph. 4:27)?**
    a. The devil
    b. Our enemies
    c. The Lord
    d. Paul

14. **Which of the following is *not* part of the "armor of God" (Eph. 6:10-18)?**
    a. Helmet of salvation
    b. Belt of truth
    c. Spear of discretion
    d. Sword of the Spirit

15. **Fill in the blank: "For to me, to live is Christ and to die is _____" (Phil. 1:21, NIV).**
    a. the devil
    b. gain
    c. suffering
    d. everything

16. **Who "made himself nothing," taking the humble position of a slave, but then was given "a name above every name," so that "every knee will bow" (Phil. 2:5-11)?**
    a. The Apostle Paul
    b. Christ Jesus

c. David

d. The righteous believer

17. Philippians 4:6 tells us not to worry about anything. What should we do instead?

a. Work hard to make a difference

b. Speak kindly to reassure one another

c. Pray about everything

d. Sleep

18. Who will "supply all your needs from his glorious riches" (Phil. 4:19)?

a. The church

b. The emperor

c. God

d. Microsoft

19. Who is "the visible image of the invisible God" (Col. 1:15)?

a. Paul

b. The believer

c. Christ

d. Your pastor

20. What doctor sends his greetings to the Colossians at the end of Paul's epistle (Col. 4:14)?

a. Paul

b. Peter

c. Luke

d. Ruth

YOU SAW IT HERE FIRST

Falling Asleep in Church

No, you're not the only one to nod off during a less-than-sizzling sermon. A young man named Eutychus (YOU-ti-kus) dozed off listening to the apostle Paul. (That should make *your* pastor feel better. Even Paul put people to sleep!) Anyway, Paul was preaching on and on—it was close to midnight—and the smoke from the flickering lamps was getting heavy, just like Eutychus's eyelids.

Unfortunately, Eutychus was sitting in a windowsill at the time. That's right, he fell three stories and died. Which would be tragic, except that Paul rushed down and brought him back to life! Then they all went back inside to eat, and Paul preached some more! Read it for yourself in Acts 20:7-12.

CRAZY ADS

Services
Get your fortune told by Esmerelda of Philippi

When it comes to predicting the future, she's a real demon! (Temporarily out of business while legal case is settled)

News Headline
Quake Rocks Jail
Unshackled Cons Stay Put
Witnesses Heard Singing

QUIZ 1E—3

1. Finish this phrase: "Believe on the Lord Jesus and you will be . . ." (Acts 16:31).
   a. taken to heaven.
   b. shielded from suffering.
   c. saved.
   d. surprised.

2. Who debated with Epicurean and Stoic philosophers in Athens?
   a. Philip
   b. Paul
   c. Philemon
   d. Plato

3. **What occupation did Paul use to make a living?**
   a. He was a blacksmith.
   b. He made tents.
   c. He was a fisherman.
   d. He taught philosophy.

4. **In what city did Demetrius the silversmith start a riot, shouting "Great is Artemis of the Ephesians!"?**
   a. Athens
   b. Ephesus
   c. Iconium
   d. Orlando

5. **Finish this verse: "It is more blessed to give than to . . ." (Acts 20:35)**
   a. steal.
   b. receive.
   c. preach.
   d. pray.

6. **A man stood before Roman Governor Felix and said, "I admit that I follow the Way" (Acts 24:14). What was the Way?**
   a. A Greek philosophy started by Aristotle
   b. A Jewish sect that had launched a rebellion in the years before Jesus
   c. An Egyptian cult that worshiped Amon and Isis and their spirits
   d. Christianity

7. **When people first saw it, they assumed Paul was a murderer getting his just reward. When he didn't die, they changed their minds and decided he was a god. What did they see?**
   a. A scar on his cheek
   b. A bird circling above him
   c. A snake that fastened on his hand
   d. A noose around his neck

8. Fill in the blank: "Whoever does not work should not
   _____" (2 Thess. 3:10).
   a. rest
   b. play
   c. eat
   d. live

9. Fill in the blank: "Don't let anyone think less of you
   because you are _____" (1 Tim. 4:12).
   a. young
   b. a minister
   c. my friend
   d. Baptist

10. What is "the root of all kinds of evil" (1 Tim. 6:10)?
    a. Money
    b. The love of money
    c. Selfishness
    d. Turnips

11. What is "inspired by God and useful to teach us"?
    (2 Tim. 3:16).
    a. All Scripture
    b. The ministry of the apostle Paul
    c. All the events of this world
    d. All of the above

12. Who is able to help us when we're tempted, because he
    has been tempted, too (Heb. 2:18)?
    a. Paul
    b. Timothy
    c. Jesus
    d. Our church minister

13. According to Hebrews 11:1 (NIV), what is "being sure of
    what we hope for and certain of what we do not see"?
    a. Temptation
    b. Salvation

c. Faith

d. Pride

14. **Who, by faith, refused to be treated as the son of Pharaoh's daughter (Heb. 11:24)?**
    a. Joseph
    b. Moses
    c. Paul
    d. Cleopatra

15. **Who assumed that if Isaac died, God was able to bring him back to life again (Heb. 11:19)?**
    a. Abraham
    b. Sarah
    c. Isaac
    d. Paul

16. **Who left home at God's command, "because he was confidently looking forward to a city with eternal foundations" (Heb. 11:10)?**
    a. Noah
    b. Abraham
    c. Moses
    d. Barnabas

17. **Fill in the blank: "Faith by itself, if it is not accompanied by action, is _____" (James 2:17, NIV).**
    a. dead
    b. an easy ride
    c. abominable
    d. wishful thinking

18. **What will happen if you "resist the devil" (James 4:7)?**
    a. You will grow stronger.
    b. He will fight you.
    c. He will flee from you.
    d. People will be impressed.

19. **Who "prowls around like a roaring lion, looking for some victim to devour" (1 Pet. 5:8)?**
    a. Adam
    b. Cain
    c. The devil
    d. Daniel

20. **Fill in the blank: "_____ is love" (1 John 4:16).**
    a. Hope
    b. God
    c. Sincerity
    d. Life

Dumb Jokes

Q: Why did the apostle Paul spend so much time in prison?
A: Because of his arresting personality.

Q: Why was Paul destined to travel so much?
A: He was born to Rome.

HIDDEN FRUIT

The nine qualities described as "fruit of the Spirit" in Galatians 5:22-23 are hidden in the following silly story. Can you find them? (Notes: We took the -*ness* suffix off some of the words. Words and names are strung between the words of the story.)

It's all over. At Hojo, you hope a cell phone will give you something to yap at. I enc—encountered a napkin delicately filled with a mysterious goo. Directions were written there, point A to point B. I proceeded by faith, full of anticipation, hoping it wasn't just a tangent. Let me tell you what I saw: Two mythic creatures—Elf C on Troll D.

Here's what you're looking for:

Love	Good
Joy	Faithful
Peace	Gentle
Patience	Self-control
Kind	

TV LISTINGS

Comedy
Leave It to Stephen

See our hero helping widows and preaching the Word. If the church needs him, he's there.

Action
The A Team

Antioch sends apostles Paul and Barnabas out to share their message with the world.

Movie of the Week
The Phantom Menace

The devil wanders like a roaring lion, seeking those he can devour.

Comedy
Rhoda

She's just the maid, but she gets into some pretty powerful scenes. See whom she leaves at the door this week!

Talk Show
The View

"From now on we regard no one from a worldly point of view. Though we once regarded Christ in this way, we do so no longer. Therefore, if anyone is in Christ, he is a new creation; the old has gone, the new has come!" (2 Cor. 5:16-17, NIV).

Drama
Providence

Once again, God promises to supply all our needs, according to his riches in Christ Jesus (Phil. 4:19).

1F
mix it up
(GENERAL INFORMATION)

QUIZ 1F—1

1. **Which of the following cities was *not* visited by Paul?**
   a. Thessalonica
   b. Thebes
   c. Troas
   d. Jerusalem

2. **Who said it to whom? "Shall I go and get one of the Hebrew women to nurse the baby for you?" (Exod. 2:7, NIV).**
   a. Hagar to her mistress Sarah
   b. Moses' sister, presumably Miriam, to Pharaoh's daughter
   c. The innkeeper to Mary
   d. Fisher to Price

3. **Which of the following plants is *not* mentioned in Scripture?**
   a. Lily
   b. Daisy
   c. Bulrush
   d. Rose

4. **Where was it said? "Take off your sandals, for the place where you are standing is holy ground" (Exod. 3:5, NIV).**
   a. At the burning bush
   b. The temple in Jerusalem
   c. In the home of Mary and Martha, when Jesus taught
   d. Payless

5. **What terrible thing happened during the reign of Judah's king Jehoiachin.**
   a. The people began worshiping Baal.
   b. An eclipse blocked the sun and many went blind.
   c. The Babylonian army conquered Jerusalem.
   d. He pierced his tongue.

6. **To whom was it said? "Let my people go" (Exod. 5:1).**
   a. The king of Babel
   b. Pharaoh
   c. Goliath
   d. Paul, preaching an especially long sermon

7. **Esther kept her nationality a secret. What was it?**
   a. She was Babylonian.
   b. She was Jewish.
   c. She was Ethiopian.
   d. She was Swedish.

8. **Who said it? "I had another dream, and this time the sun and moon and eleven stars were bowing down to me" (Gen. 37:9, NIV).**
   a. Pharaoh
   b. Ezekiel
   c. The apostle John
   d. Joseph

9. **One of the churches of the book of Revelation shares a name with a major U.S. city. Which one?**
   a. Providence
   b. Philadelphia
   c. Utica
   d. Wheaton

10. **Who said it? "The voice is the voice of Jacob, but the hands are the hands of Esau" (Gen. 27:22, NIV).**
    a. Their father Isaac
    b. Their uncle Laban
    c. God
    d. The prophet Ezekiel, describing the waywardness of his people

11. **Where did Abraham come from (Gen. 11:31)?**
    a. Ur
    b. Uz

c. Ai

d. Uh–oh

12. Who said it? "And now let Pharaoh look for a discerning and wise man and put him in charge of the land of Egypt" (Gen. 41:33, NIV).

a. Sarah, the visitor from Canaan

b. Joseph, the prisoner

c. David, the king

d. Harvey, the consultant

13. Which of the following was *not* an associate of Paul?

a. Aurelius

b. Luke

c. Titus

d. Epaphras

14. Who said it? "Very well . . . I will go with you. But since you have made this choice, you will receive no honor. For the Lord's victory over Sisera will be at the hands of a woman" (Judg. 4:9).

a. Deborah

b. Rachel

c. Sisera

d. Samuel

15. Which of the following was a feast observed by the Israelites?

a. The Feast of Gratitude, or Praise

b. The Feast of Tabernacles, or Booths

c. The Feast of Wells, or Water

d. The Feast of Stephen

16. **Who said it? "I have been taking care of my father's sheep. . . . When a lion or bear comes to steal a lamb from the flock, I go after it with a club and take the lamb from its mouth. . . . I have done this to both lions and bears, and I'll do it to this pagan Philistine, too, for he has defied the armies of the living God!" (1 Sam. 17:34-36).**
    a. Moses
    b. David
    c. Amos
    d. Barnum

17. **Of all the priests mentioned in Scripture, who had the shortest name?**
    a. Og
    b. Eli
    c. Nun
    d. Jehoiada

18. **To whom was this reported? "Things are not going well for those who returned to the province of Judah. They are in great trouble and disgrace. The wall of Jerusalem has been torn down, and the gates have been burned" (Neh. 1:3-4).**
    a. Solomon
    b. Nehemiah
    c. Jonah
    d. Barnabas

19. **What book of the Bible has the fewest verses?**
    a. Ezra
    b. Nahum
    c. 2 John
    d. King Saul's Guide to Mental Health

20. **Who said it? "Am I a dog . . . that you come at me with a stick?" (1 Sam. 17:43, NIV).**
    a. Pharaoh
    b. Goliath
    c. Ahab
    d. Scooby-Doo

AMAZING FACTS

Moses followed God's instructions when he made a bronze serpent during a snakebite crisis. He raised the sculpture on a pole, and if people looked at it, they would live (Num. 21:4-9). Yet centuries later, some Israelites were worshiping *the bronze serpent!* King Hezekiah was finally told to break it into pieces (2 Kings 18:4).

Dumb Jokes

Q: Who's the shortest man in the Bible?
A: The soldier who slept on his watch (Matt. 28:13).

Q: Who's the second shortest man in the Bible?
A: Bildad the shoe-height (Shuhite—see Job 2:11).

Q: Who's the third shortest man in the Bible?
A: Knee-high-miah (Nehemiah)

MINI-QUIZ: HOW DO YOU MEASURE UP?

These nine questions (with some variations) have been on polls that determined how well people knew the Bible. Each question indicates the percentage of Americans who got it right. Answers are in the back of the book on page 394. How do you fare?

1. **(62%) The book of Isaiah is in . . .**
    a. the Old Testament
    b. the New Testament
    c. the garage

2. (31%) The proverb "God helps those who help themselves" is . . .
  a. in the Bible
  b. not in the Bible
  c. the reason I pig out at church suppers

3. (48%) The book of Jonah is . . .
  a. in the Bible
  b. not in the Bible
  c. a whale of a story

4. (52%) The book of Thomas is . . .
  a. in the Bible
  b. not in the Bible
  c. better than the sequel

5. (61%) Jesus Christ was born in . . .
  a. Jerusalem
  b. Nazareth
  c. Bethlehem
  d. Cleveland

6. (70%) How many apostles were there?
  a. Three
  b. Seven
  c. Twelve
  d. Twenty
  e. More than Paul could write by himself

7. (42%) Who delivered the Sermon on the Mount?
  a. Moses
  b. Jesus
  c. Sir Edmund Hillary
  d. UPS

8. (46%) What are the names of the four Gospels?

9. (42%) Can you name five of the Ten Commandments?

QUIZ 1F—2

Most of the following excuses are lame, but a couple of them are truly excusable. Who gave the following excuses? Which ones are the good ones, and which are the bad ones? (All Scripture verses are NIV.)

1. **"The woman you put here with me—she gave me some fruit from the tree, and I ate it"** (Gen. 3:12).
   a. The serpent
   b. John the Baptist
   c. Adam
   d. Johnny Appleseed

2. **"The serpent deceived me, and I ate"** (Gen. 3:13).
   a. Adam
   b. Eve
   c. Judas
   d. Indiana Jones

3. **"It is not our custom here to give the younger daughter in marriage before the older one. Finish this daughter's bridal week; then we will give you the younger one also, in return for another seven years of work"** (Gen. 29:26-27).
   a. Rebekah
   b. Laban
   c. Esau
   d. Solomon

4. **"You know how prone these people are to evil. They said to me, 'Make us gods who will go before us. As for this fellow Moses who brought us up out of Egypt, we don't know what has happened to him.' So I told them, 'Whoever has any gold jewelry, take it off.' Then they gave me the gold, and I threw it into the fire, and out came this calf!"** (Exod. 32:22-24).
   a. Aaron
   b. Pharaoh
   c. Caleb
   d. Elsie

5. "When I saw that the men were scattering, and that you did not come at the set time, and that the Philistines were assembling at Micmash, I thought, 'Now the Philistines will come down against me at Gilgal, and I have not sought the Lord's favor.' So I felt compelled to offer the burnt offering" (1 Sam. 13:11-12).
   a. Samuel
   b. David
   c. Goliath
   d. Saul

6. "But I did obey the Lord. . . . I went on the mission the Lord assigned me. I completely destroyed the Amalekites and brought back Agag their king. The soldiers took sheep and cattle from the plunder, the best of what was devoted to God, in order to sacrifice them to the Lord your God at Gilgal" (1 Sam. 15:20-21).
   a. Joshua
   b. Saul
   c. Ahab
   d. Magog

7. "I have been very zealous for the Lord God Almighty. The Israelites have rejected your covenant, broken down your altars, and put your prophets to death with the sword. I am the only one left, and now they are trying to kill me too" (1 Kings 19:10).
   a. Elijah
   b. Jeremiah
   c. John the Baptist
   d. Jezebel

8. "Master . . . I knew that you are a hard man, harvesting where you have not sown and gathering where you have not scattered seed. So I was afraid and went out and hid your talent in the ground. See, here is what belongs to you" (Matt. 25:24-25).
   a. Lazarus

b. Simon Peter

c. Thomas

d. A nameless servant in one of Jesus' parables

9. **"Why were you searching for me? . . . Didn't you know I had to be in my Father's house?" (Luke 2:49).**

    a. Josiah

    b. Mary

    c. Jesus

    d. Timothy

10. **"I planned to visit you on my way to Macedonia and to come back to you from Macedonia. . . . I call God as my witness that it was in order to spare you that I did not return to Corinth. So I made up my mind that I would not make another painful visit to you" (2 Cor. 1:16, 23; 2:1).**

    a. Daniel

    b. Jesus

    c. Paul

    d. Alexander

AMAZING FACTS

Two words have come straight from Hebrew into scores of other languages: *Amen* and *Hallelujah*.

The word *Bible* comes from the Greek *biblos,* which refers to any book.

That Greek word *biblos* comes from the city of Byblos, where papyrus grew. Papyrus was used to make a kind of paper.

Dumb Jokes

Q: What kind of deal did Ruth get when she tried to buy food?

A: They took her to the gleaners.

MINI-QUIZ: WEATHER MATCHING
Which weather condition . . .

1. floated a portable zoo?	a. Bright cloud
2. made Joseph prime minister of Egypt?	b. Whirlwind
3. parted the Red Sea	c. Sun standing still
4. plagued Egypt in Moses' day	d. Flood
5. led the Israelites through the desert	e. Storm
6. helped Joshua win a battle	f. Drought
7. fleeced Gideon into leading his people	g. Wind
8. gave Elijah and Ahab something to talk about	h. Dew
9. was Elijah's ride to God's side	i. Hail
10. introduced Jonah to the whale	j. Famine

HIDDEN BIBLE WOMEN
The names of sixteen Bible women are hidden in this very silly story. Can you find them? (Note: Words and names are strung between the words of the story.)

She was stuck in a rut. Her bankcard didn't work (she had forgotten whether she made B or A her PIN's last character). Her apartment was boiling because her German handyman never fixed her AC (he loved to put things off).

She quickly dialed his number. Nice, she thought. If I were smart, having air-conditioning would be unnecessary.

"Ja? 'ello?" he answered.

"Can you—?"

"Lah lah lah lah lah." (From Aryan roots comes the ability to yodel.)

"I—"

"Lah lah lah lah lah."

She hung up. With that racket he makes, there's no stopping him.

For a habitual treat on the Sabbath, she barreled over to the Speedway. When they rev engines, a *rahummmm* sound makes such a din, a hearing person could have trouble. Aha! Maybe that was the whole problem.

Here's what you're looking for:

Bathsheba	Leah
Bernice	Lydia
Deborah	Martha
Delilah	Mary
Dinah	Rachel
Esther	Rahab
Eve	Ruth
Jael	Sarah

MINI-QUIZ: WORDS AND PHRASES

1. Which of the following phrases appears in the Bible?
   a. A stitch in time saves nine.
   b. Honesty is the best policy.
   c. Turn the other cheek.
   d. No right on red.

2. Which of the following phrases appears in the Bible?
   a. Spare the rod and spoil the child.
   b. Beggars can't be choosers.
   c. Rob Peter to pay Paul.
   d. The quicker picker-upper.

3. Which of the following phrases appears in the Bible?
   a. Cleanliness is next to godliness.
   b. Salt of the earth
   c. Strike while the iron is hot.
   d. *I* before *E* except after *C*

4. Which of the following phrases appears in the Bible?
   a. Charity begins at home.
   b. Everything that glitters is not gold.
   c. Thorn in the flesh
   d. $e = mc^2$

5. What word is used most often in the Bible?
    a. God
    b. Grace
    c. Holy
    d. The

AMAZING FACTS

For centuries in England, Scotland, and Holland, Christians have practiced "dipping" on New Year's Day. They open their Bibles and close their eyes, pointing to a verse, which they take as God's message to them for the coming year.

Dumb Jokes

(Here's an old one)
One young man practiced "dipping" (see above) with bad results. The first verse he pointed to was Matthew 27:5—"Then Judas . . . went out and hanged himself."

    That wasn't a good verse for him, so he tried again, pointing to Luke 10:37—"Now go and do the same."

    Something was desperately wrong, so he tried again, flipping randomly to John 13:27—"Hurry. Do it now."

MINI-QUIZ: WATER
These people had trouble with water. Can you name them?

1. He had a forty-day rain.
2. He walked on water—then got that sinking feeling.
3. He should have asked the rock nicely for water.
4. This well-to-do patriarch kept losing his wells to his neighbors and digging new ones.
5. She asked her son for wine when the wedding had only water.
6. He talked the crew into tossing him overboard.

MINI-QUIZ: FEET

1. **Who was told to take off his sandals because he stood on holy ground?**
   a. Abraham
   b. Moses
   c. David
   d. Dr. Scholl

2. **Who healed a lame man at the Beautiful Gate of the temple?**
   a. Nehemiah
   b. Jesus
   c. Peter and John
   d. George Clooney

3. **Who got new sandals when he returned home?**
   a. David
   b. The Prodigal Son
   c. Timothy
   d. Tommy Hilfiger

4. **A woman moistened Jesus' feet with her tears and wiped them dry with what?**
   a. A servant's towel
   b. Her hands
   c. Her hair
   d. A hair dryer

5. **Who said he was not worthy to carry Jesus' sandals?**
   a. John the Baptist
   b. Peter
   c. Pilate
   d. Sid, the sandal-carrier

6. **According to Romans 10:15, who have beautiful feet?**
   a. The saints in heaven
   b. Those who bring good news

c. Egyptians

d. Joggers

7. Who at first refused to let Jesus wash his feet?

a. John the Baptist

b. Judas

c. Peter

d. Asa

AMAZING FACTS

In the fifteenth century, someone published a comic-book Bible. The *Biblia Pauperum* or "Bible for the Poor" contained pictures of different biblical scenes with brief notes of explanation.

FAQ

Q: Why do Christians put fish on their car bumpers?

A: The fish is an ancient Christian symbol because the Greek word for fish—*ichthus*—is an acronym for several biblical titles of Jesus.

Jesus = *Iesous*

Christ = *CHristos*

God's = *THeou*

Son = *Uios*

Savior = *Soter*

MINI-QUIZ: PEOPLE WHO PRAYED

Pick the six right answers from the ten provided.

___1. He prayed that his brother wouldn't kill him.

___2. He asked God why they had lost their second battle in Canaan.

___3. He prayed that his servant would see and his enemies be blinded.

___4. He prayed when he learned he was terminally ill . . . and God changed his mind.

___5. The church gathered in Mary's home, praying for his release from prison.

___6. They prayed and sang hymns in prison.

a. Peter (Acts 12)
b. Joshua (Josh. 7)
c. David (Ps. 51)
d. Jacob (Gen. 32:9-12)
e. Timothy and Titus (1 Tim. 6)
f. Elisha (2 Kings 6)
g. Isaiah (Isa. 6)
h. Paul and Silas (Acts 16)
i. Hezekiah (2 Chron. 32)
j. Moses (Deut. 6)

SMART JOKES

It's one of the funniest moments in Scripture. Haman, the king's right-hand man, hates Mordecai, the gatekeeper. In fact he's planning to have Mordecai killed. But Mordecai has shown loyalty to the king by warning him of a plot against his life. So King Xerxes calls Haman and asks, "What should I do to honor a man who truly pleases me?"

Haman thinks the king is talking about *him,* so he pulls out all the stops. Give the man a royal robe, Haman suggests, and the king's own horse. Have a nobleman lead the man through the city, shouting, "This is what happens to those the king wishes to honor!"

"Excellent!" the king replies. "Do that for Mordecai." So Haman himself has to lead the man he hates through the streets of the city, shouting his praises.

This is just one of many great stories in the Bible. Read this one for yourself in Esther 6.

MINI-QUIZ: PEOPLE WHO CRIED

Match the description with the right name.

____1. This brother cried when he resolved a feud with his other brother.
____2. This man cried at the death of his rebellious son.
____3. This mother-in-law cried with her two daughters-in-law when it was time to leave.
____4. This prophet cried when he foresaw the terrible things a future king would do.

___ 5. This man cried when he saw his younger brother after a long time apart.

___ 6. This woman cried because she didn't know where Jesus was.

___ 7. This man cried at the tomb of his friend Lazarus.

___ 8. This disciple cried after he had pretended to be ignorant.

___ 9. This future leader cried when his adoptive mother opened a basket.

___10. This friend cried when saying good-bye to David.

a. Naomi (Ruth 1:9)

b. Jesus (John 11:35)

c. Esau (Gen. 33:4)

d. Peter (Matt. 26:75)

e. Jonathan (1 Sam. 20:41)

f. Joseph (Gen. 43:30)

g. Mary Magdalene (John 20:11)

h. David (2 Sam. 19:1-4)

i. Moses (Exod. 2:6)

j. Elisha (2 Kings 8:11)

AMAZING FACTS

Ten of the 20 most common male names in the U.S. are biblical names, but only three of the top 20 female names are from the Bible.

The Sons of Thunder would be happy to know that *James* and *John* are most popular with men, with *Michael* (after the archangel) in fourth place and *David* in sixth. *Mary* is the most popular female name, with *Elizabeth* at number 5.

Here are the names (in order of ranking) that made the Top 25 on both sides:

Male	Female
1. James	1. Mary
2. John	5. Elizabeth
4. Michael	19. Ruth
6. David	20. Sharon (a place name in Scripture)
9. Joseph	23. Sarah
10. Thomas	25. Deborah
12. Daniel	
13. Paul	
14. Mark	
18. Steven	

PART 2:

stuff you didn't know you knew

2A
start-up

(GENESIS — 1 SAMUEL)

QUIZ 2A—1

1. What reason did God give for creating woman?
   a. People must be fruitful and multiply.
   b. Man had sinned and fallen short of God's glory.
   c. It is not good for the man to be alone.
   d. Without woman, man will never stop and ask for directions.

2. What did God say would happen if Adam and Eve ate from the "tree of the knowledge of good and evil"?
   a. They would die.
   b. They would get very sick and pray for healing.
   c. They would turn into serpents.
   d. They would turn into lawyers.

3. Who said it? "Did God really say you must not eat any of the fruit in the garden?" (Gen. 3:1).
   a. Adam
   b. Eve
   c. The serpent
   d. The gardener

4. After what event was this said? "I will never again curse the earth, destroying all living things, even though people's thoughts and actions are bent toward evil from childhood" (Gen. 8:21).
   a. The sin of Adam and Eve
   b. The murder of Abel by Cain
   c. The flood
   d. The sinking of the *Titanic*

5. What was Noah's relation to Shem, Ham, and Japheth (JAY-feth)?
   a. It was his favorite breakfast.
   b. They were his sons.
   c. In Hebrew, they're the three types of animals on the ark.
   d. After the forty-day blizzard, they were the front line of the hockey team he coached.

6. **Noah sent two creatures out of the ark to check the conditions. What were they?**
   a. Shem and Japheth
   b. Fruit flies
   c. A raven and a dove
   d. A tortoise and a hare

7. **God punished the builders of Babel in an appropriate-sounding way. What did he do?**
   a. What they were building fell on them
   b. They could never finish what they started.
   c. He confused their speech, so they "babbled" to one another.
   d. Government regulations

8. **To whom was it said? "Take your son, your only son . . . and go to the land of Moriah. Sacrifice him there as a burnt offering" (Gen. 22:2).**
   a. Cain
   b. Abraham
   c. Ahab
   d. Mary

9. **When she was told she would have a baby, what did the ninety-year-old Sarah do?**
   a. She laughed out loud.
   b. She quit her job.
   c. She forced everyone in the room to kneel in prayer.
   d. She promised to name the baby Abraham Jr.

10. **In the first few verses of the Bible, what is described as "formless and empty"?**
   a. The earth
   b. The ocean
   c. Adam's heart
   d. Adam's stomach

11. In the first chapter of Genesis, what did God call "very good"?

a. The hearts of Adam and Eve
b. All he had made
c. The names the man gave to the birds and beasts
d. The chances that Adam and Eve would mess things up

12. What did Adam call "bone of my bones and flesh of my flesh" (NIV)?

a. A gorilla
b. His reflection in the Kishon River
c. His first knee injury
d. Eve

13. Cain was a farmer, so he didn't offer the same kind of sacrifice as his brother. What was Abel's occupation?

a. Shepherd
b. Blacksmith
c. Warrior
d. Accountant

14. God asked, "Where is your brother Abel?" What was Cain's reply?

a. "You're asking me?"
b. "I am not Abel to answer."
c. "At the altar with his sacrifice"
d. "Am I my brother's keeper?"

15. What is the significance of the number 969 to the man named Methuselah?

a. The number of children he had
b. The number of years he lived
c. The number of times he walked around the Promised Land
d. He invented that number.

16. **To whom was it said? "I will cause you to become the father of a great nation. I will bless you and make you famous, and I will make you a blessing to others" (Gen. 12:2).**
    a. Adam and Eve
    b. Abraham
    c. Ahasuerus
    d. Amerigo Vespucci

17. **When they got to the Promised Land, Abraham and his nephew Lot had to choose the area where they'd settle. Which of them chose the lush area near the city of Sodom?**
    a. Abraham
    b. Lot
    c. They both settled near Sodom.
    d. They both stayed far away from that wicked city.

18. **Why was Lot's wife turned into a pillar of salt?**
    a. She looked back at the city of Sodom as it was being destroyed.
    b. She nagged Lot about leaving Sodom before it was destroyed.
    c. She laughed when God threaten to destroy the city.
    d. She had too much sodium in her diet.

19. **While his brother Esau loved hunting, Jacob had a different pastime. What was it?**
    a. Fishing
    b. Farming
    c. Cooking
    d. Needlepoint

20. **Esau was nicknamed Edom, which means "Red." Why?**
    a. He *was* red.
    b. He loved to shed blood.
    c. He loved to eat red stew.
    d. The "Blue" nickname was already taken.

YOU SAW IT HERE FIRST

Embalming

Egyptians were masters at embalming dead bodies, so it's no surprise that Joseph was embalmed (Gen. 50:26). After all, in his later life he had been Egypt's prime minister. But his father Jacob, who moved to Egypt to rejoin his famous son, was also embalmed (Gen. 50:2), and Joseph made a special trip back to Canaan to bury him. Centuries later, when the Israelites escaped slavery in Egypt, they took Joseph's bones with them (Exod. 13:19).

Acid Rain?

The cities of Sodom and Gomorrah were destroyed when "the Lord rained down burning sulfur from the heavens." Interestingly, the nearby Dead Sea is still known for extremely high mineral content. (And remember that Lot's wife became a "pillar of salt.")

BRAIN STUFF

Q: What Bible characters had no parents?

A: Adam and Eve, certainly. But also the mysterious Melchizedek, of whom the book of Hebrews says, "There is no record of his father or mother or any of his ancestors" (Heb. 7:3). You could also say Joshua, who was the son of Nun (none?).

Q: Did Adam and Eve have navels?

A: Why would they?

CRAZY ADS

Calendar

My Life by **Methuselah**

A page-a-year calendar with 969 pages

Hit Song

"You Gotta Move When the Spirit Says Move"

by Abram and the Ur-folk

Service
Ramshackle Animal Supply
When you need a sacrifice right *now!* Delivery to Mount Moriah and surrounding mounts.

Product
Bless and Moan Eyeglasses
So your sneaky son won't pull the wool over your eyes.

Dumb Jokes
Q: What did Abraham say after his nephew chose the better land?
A: "Thanks a Lot!"

Q: What kind of wood was the ark made out of?
A: 2 x 2s

Q: Why couldn't Cain bring God a sacrifice from his flocks?
A: He wasn't Abel.

Q: How did Lot's wife become so well known in Sodom?
A: She became a pillar of the community.

MINI-QUIZ: FAMOUS FIRSTS

1. Who was the first murderer? (Gen. 4:8)

2. Who was the first shepherd? (Gen 4:2)

3. Who planted the first garden? (Gen. 2:8)

4. Who planted the first vineyard, probably in soggy ground? (Gen. 9:20)

5. What's the first color mentioned in the Bible? (Gen. 1:30)

QUIZ 2A—2

1. Jacob left home in a hurry, toward his uncle Laban's estate. Why?
   a. Laban was hiring herdsmen.
   b. Famine was about to hit Canaan.
   c. Esau was trying to kill him.
   d. The new Beanie Baby camels were going on sale.

2. What did Jacob have to do to marry Laban's daughter Rachel?
   a. Work for Laban for seven years
   b. Prove his courage by making peace with Esau
   c. Dig seven new wells for Rachel's flocks
   d. Bring her flowers

3. After the wedding, Jacob had a major surprise. What was it?
   a. Rachel just wanted his money.
   b. He had actually married Rachel's sister, Leah.
   c. During the wedding feast, Laban had stolen all his flocks.
   d. Rachel looked awful without makeup.

4. Joseph had dreams that annoyed his brothers. What did he dream about?
   a. The sun, moon, and stars bowing down to Joseph's star
   b. Sheaves of grain burning up in the fields
   c. Fat and skinny cows in the Nile River
   d. Little people dancing on a yellow brick road

5. Joseph's brothers wanted to kill him, but Judah suggested doing what instead?
   a. Scaring him and sending him back home
   b. Stealing his coat and burning it
   c. Selling him as a slave
   d. Forcing him to listen to bagpipe music

6. Why was Joseph thrown into an Egyptian prison?
   a. He killed an Egyptian slave master.
   b. He was falsely accused of attacking his master's wife.
   c. He spoke critical words against the pharaoh.
   d. He was unwittingly involved in a pyramid scheme.

7. Who else was in prison with Joseph?
   a. Potiphar and his wife
   b. Pharaoh's baker and cup-bearer
   c. Pharaoh's brother and the royal astrologer
   d. Reuben and Benjamin

8. During the famine, Joseph's brothers came to Egypt to buy grain. They bowed down in front of an Egyptian official. Who was it?
   a. Pharaoh
   b. Joseph
   c. Moses
   d. Rameses

9. When the Israelites were slaves in Egypt, what was their main job?
   a. Making bricks and mortar
   b. Dredging the Nile
   c. Caring for Egyptian children
   d. Selling insurance

10. What hot headed action forced Moses to flee Egypt?
   a. He yelled at Pharaoh for his treatment of the Israelites.
   b. He gave the Israelites straw to help them make bricks.
   c. He killed an Egyptian slave master for mistreating an Israelite.
   d. He cut off the Sphinx's nose.

11. When Moses pleaded for someone to help him face the pharaoh, whom did God choose?
   a. His sister, Miriam
   b. His brother, Aaron

    c. His boyhood chum Rameses

    d. A talking donkey

12. God told Moses to throw his staff on the ground. What did it turn into?

    a. Bread

    b. Water

    c. A snake

    d. Trick question: It was still a staff.

13. How did Pharaoh respond to Moses' demands?

    a. He immediately agreed to everything they asked for.

    b. He threw Moses and Aaron in prison.

    c. He stopped giving the Israelites straw to make bricks.

    d. All of the above.

14. God sent ten plagues upon Egypt to force Pharaoh to release the Israelites. Which of the following was one of the ten plagues?

    a. The Nile River turned to blood.

    b. The Red Sea turned to blood.

    c. The Pools of Rameses turned to wine.

    d. All wine in the kingdom turned to blood.

15. What body of water did Joshua instruct the Israelites to cross to get to the Promised Land?

    a. The Red Sea

    b. The Black Sea

    c. The Jordan River

    d. The Pacific Ocean

16. Of the Ten Commandments, how many say (in the King James Version) "Thou shalt not"?

    a. All ten

    b. Eight

    c. None

    d. Trick question: There are actually eleven commandments.

17. **While Moses was on the mountain receiving God's law, what trouble was his brother Aaron getting into?**
    a. Leading a rebellion against Moses
    b. Leading the people back to Egypt
    c. Making an idol for the people to worship
    d. Gluing Moses' sandals to the tent floor

18. **Which is the first of the Ten Commandments?**
    a. "Do not worship any other gods besides me."
    b. "Do not commit adultery."
    c. "Honor your father and mother."
    d. "No right turn on red."

19. **Something in ancient Israel was made of acacia wood, measuring about four feet by two feet by two feet. What was it?**
    a. The altar in the tabernacle
    b. The ark of the covenant
    c. Moses' staff that miraculously budded
    d. The cars in the first Soap Box Derby

20. **What destructive act did Moses do when he saw the golden calf?**
    a. He smashed the idol with a hammer.
    b. He threw the stone tablets of the law to the ground and broke them.
    c. He slew his brother, Aaron.
    d. He started smoking.

AMAZING FACTS

The golden calf was probably a bull, which was worshiped in Egypt and other Mideast cultures.

YOU SAW IT HERE FIRST

Degrees of Murder

Our modern legal system has degrees of certain crimes, especially murder. First-degree murder is the stuff of headlines and movies. Manslaughter charges are for accidental loss of life and carry a less severe penalty. Old Testament Law makes similar distinctions, considering the intentions of the killer (Exod. 21; Num. 35:16-21).

8-ball?

Do you remember this toy? You're suppose to ask the 8-ball a question and then shake it up—a cryptic message appears at the top. Of course, it's just a silly game for kids. But the Israelites had a strange way of deciding things that was something like that. There were two gems on the high priest's breastplate known as Urim and Thummim (Exod. 28:30). These gems were supposed to help the high priest know what God wanted. We don't know how they worked, whether they glowed or were rolled like dice, but God used them to guide his people.

CRAZY ADS

Product
Helpmark Cards and Gifts

When you've double-crossed someone and you don't want them to kill you. Specializing in the reconciliation of twin brothers.

Product
Sphinx

The home-management computer program for the finest households in Egypt

Product
NaFrisko Cereals

Get grain during a famine without having to prove you're not spies. Distributorships in Canaan and Egypt.

Book
The Canaan Prophecies.
A boy's dreams. Mystical revelations to the youngest of twelve brothers. Captivating.

Magazine
Household Beautiful
• Tips for everything but the kitchen sphinx
• Day trips along the Nile
• When your master's wife wants extra service you can't provide

Video Game
Spynab
Keep hiding the silver cup in your brother's sack until he figures out who you really are.

Dumb Jokes

Rhymers
Q: Why couldn't Eve find her pet butterflies?
A: Adam had 'em

Q: What was Adam doing to keep the Garden lookin' good?
A: Weedin' Eden

Q: Possibly the cause of Abel's death?
A: Cain's pain

Q: What got Noah's sandals dirty after forty days of rain?
A: Flood mud

Q: What did Noah do on Mount Ararat?
A: Parked the ark

Q: What happened when all the people on the ark had lunch?
A: Eight ate

Q: What happened when Jacob looked up from the stew he was making?
A: He saw Esau

Q: What did Moses enjoy doing to his brother?
A: Scarin' Aaron

Q: What did Moses' wife, Zipporah, get for Valentine's Day?
A: Moses' roses

Q: The official bird of Egypt?
A: Pharaoh's sparrow

Q: What was Jericho's disaster?
A: Wall fall

Q: What might the elderly Naomi be jealous of?
A: Ruth's youth

Q: How tall was the toddler Samuel?
A: Knee-high to Eli

HIDDEN MOSES

The following nonsense story hides ten words or names associated with Moses. Can you find them? (Note: Words and names are strung between the words of the story.)

One boring day I take the bus home. As a bull rushes toward red capes, I naively run for public transportation. Those bus fares sure gyp the rider. I take a tattered seat next to an alcoholic man named Ronald, just coming home from AA. Ron tells me he's been on that Russian spacecraft Mir—I am not making this up. And after all that hoopla, guess what? I'm still bored.

Here's what you're looking for:

Aaron   Miriam
Bullrushes   Nebo
Bush   Plagues
Egypt   Red Sea
Manna   Sinai

QUIZ 2A—3

1. **Who said it? "When they brought [their gold earrings] to me, I threw them into the fire—and out came this calf!" (Exod. 32:24).**
    a. Moses
    b. Aaron
    c. Abraham
    d. Roy Rogers

2. **When Moses came down from Mount Sinai, what did he look like (Exod. 34:29)?**
    a. Charlton Heston
    b. His face glowed.
    c. Much older
    d. Much younger

3. **The prophet Balaam was riding his donkey to Moab, to offer his services to a rival king. Who complained about what Balaam was doing?**
    a. Joshua
    b. Moses
    c. Balaam's wife
    d. Balaam's donkey

4. **Why did the Israelites have to wander so long in the wilderness?**
    a. To throw the Egyptian army off their trail
    b. Because they refused to enter the Promised Land when they had the chance

c. God was preparing the land of Canaan for an easy conquest.

d. Moses wouldn't stop and ask for directions.

5. **One day a year the high priest entered the Holy of Holies in the tabernacle (and later the temple) to offer sacrifices for the sins of the people. What was this day called?**
   a. The Day of Atonement
   b. The Day of Remembrance
   c. The Sabbath
   d. It had no special name.

6. **Mount Nebo overlooked the Promised Land. Who died there?**
   a. Joshua
   b. Moses
   c. Abraham
   d. Sir Edmund Hillary

7. **Finish this verse: "Love the Lord your God with all your . . ." (Deut. 6:6)**
   a. heart, all your soul, and all your strength.
   b. family, and love your neighbors as your own children.
   c. goods, and give him the abundance of your crops, a tenth thereof.
   d. baseball cards, all your marbles, and every last stick of gum.

8. **When the Israelites entered the Promised Land, the priests carrying the ark of the covenant went first. What happened when they set foot in the Jordan River?**
   a. The water turned red.
   b. The water stopped flowing so they could cross on dry ground.
   c. The priests were struck dead for touching the ark.
   d. The priests all said, "Yow-*wee!* That's *cold!*"

9. **A woman named Rahab helped the Israelites conquer the Promised Land. How?**
    a. She stabbed the king of Bethel with a dagger.
    b. She gave Joshua the plans to Jerusalem's water system.
    c. She hid two Israelite spies from the king of Jericho.
    d. She fortified the troops with her amazing chicken soup.

10. **The first three judges mentioned in the book of Judges are:**
    a. Shadrach, Meshach, and Abednego
    b. Othniel, Ehud, and Shamgar
    c. Samuel, Samson, and Saul
    d. Peter, Paul, and Mary

11. **Who said it? "No, my lord! . . . We have come to buy food. We are all brothers and honest men, sir! We are not spies!" (Gen. 42:10).**
    a. Cain and Abel to the people of Babel
    b. Jacob's sons to their brother Joseph
    c. Joshua and Caleb to Rahab
    d. Mulder and Scully

12. **Which of the following is *not* true of Deborah?**
    a. She was the only woman among the judges of Israel.
    b. She led the Israelites in battle against the great general Sisera.
    c. She killed Sisera by driving a tent peg through his head.
    d. She sang a song of victory that takes up a whole chapter of Judges.

13. **Gideon was sheepish about asking God twice to verify his instructions. What did he want God to do?**
    a. Send fire from heaven to consume his sacrifice
    b. Make a lamb's fleece wet with dew but the ground dry, then the opposite
    c. Speak to him in a dream
    d. E-mail him

14. When Gideon first assembled his army of 32,000, what speech did he give them?

a. You serve a great God, so victory is yours!

b. Be strong and courageous!

c. God has given us this land; it's up to us to take it!

d. If you're timid or afraid, go home.

15. How was Gideon's army reduced from 10,000 to 300?

a. He took them to a stream and watched how they drank water.

b. He only took the tallest ones.

c. A plague wiped them out.

d. He observed which soldiers kept the Sabbath.

16. How did Samson use foxes to destroy his enemies' crops?

a. He didn't feed the foxes for three days, then set the hungry foxes loose.

b. He tied the foxes' tails together around torches and sent them through the fields.

c. He made the foxes dig holes under the fields.

d. The foxes talked his enemies out of harvesting their fields.

17. With what unlikely weapon did Samson kill a thousand Philistines?

a. His hair

b. Goliath's sword

c. A donkey's jawbone

d. A B-52 bomber

18. "In those days Israel had no king, so the people did whatever seemed right in their own eyes." This is the last verse of what book?

a. Genesis

b. Judges

c. 2 Kings

d. Trump

19. What was the relation of Boaz to Ruth?
a. He was a distant relative who eventually married her.
b. He was the employer who fired her for stealing grain.
c. He was the second husband of her mother-in-law, Naomi.
d. He was the agent who signed her to a book deal.

20. Who wanted to be called Mara (which means "bitter")?
a. Ruth
b. Esther
c. Naomi
d. Bartholomew

YOU SAW IT HERE FIRST

Legal Change of Venue

Nowadays a defendant will often request a "change of venue," moving a trial to a different area in order to overcome local prejudice and assure a fair trial. That's sort of what the Old Testament "cities of refuge" did. If you accidentally killed or injured someone, their family and friends might take swift vengeance on you—even if you intended no harm. But if you could flee to one of six designated cities of refuge, you'd be safe there until a priest could conduct a fair trial (Num. 35:11-28).

Lisping

The Israelites had an internal squabble in the time of the judges. The tribe of Ephraim rebelled against judge Jephthah, but their speech impediment did them in. Jephthah's troops captured a key territory, and many Ephraimites tried to sneak away. When they were caught, they'd go through an interesting interrogation:

"'Are you a member of the tribe of Ephraim?' they would ask. If the man said, 'No, I'm not,' they would tell him to say 'Shibboleth.' If he was from Ephraim, he would say 'Sibboleth,' because people from Ephraim cannot pronounce the word correctly" (Judg. 12:5-6).

That would be very funny if not for what happened next. If the guy said "Sibboleth," they killed him. The word *Shibboleth,* Hebrew for a current of water, has entered our language as an identifying word or phrase.

CRAZY ADS

Official Document

Egyptian Centers for Disease Control

ALERT—The Nile turning to blood has caused a major health crisis for the entire region. The ecosystem has collapsed, sending frogs into the land, where they die for lack of water, drawing flies. Strangely unaffected: The land of Goshen, where the Israelite slaves live. The Justice Department is investigating possible terrorist activities.

Magazine

Desert Camping

• Retirement Tips: You might be out there 40 years
• Raising Canaan: Don't go for the grasshopper talk
• Quail Was Right! Catching and roasting those heavenly birds
• Packing Clothes for Hot Days, Cool Nights
• "That Cloud Is So Bright I Have to Wear Shades"
• Tabernacle Etiquette
• 50 Quick-and-Easy Recipes for Manna!

Web Site

www.wander.com

Follow the Israelites' progress through the wilderness.

Book

Leadership by Joshua bar-Nun

How to take twelve selfish tribes and make a nation

Video Game

Wall Fall

March around Jericho until its walls fall down

Product

Willite Authentic Lamb's Wool Fleece

Recommended by General Gideon . . . for that can-dew spirit

CD

Midianite Train to Georgia by Gideon's Trumpet Chorus

Including "Pretty as a Pitcher" and other torch songs

Web Site
www.feastorfamine.org
• A dating service especially for young widows
• There's a harvest of eligible men out there. Glean a guy today!
• Serving Moab, Edom, and the greater Judean area

Dumb Jokes

Q: What kind of jeans to Israel's priests wear?
A: Levi's

Q: Why couldn't Pharaoh afford to pull his chariots out of the water?
A: He was in the Red, see?

Q: Why did God have to send the Israelites bread from heaven?
A: Because all they did was loaf around.

Q: What was the shortened version of the law Moses received on Mount Sinai?
A: Cliff Notes

Q: What happened when the man counting all the Israelites went on vacation?
A: He took leave of his census.

Q: Why did Gideon have success in his battles?
A: He was following the wool of God.

Q: How do we know Samson was a hit with the audience during his last performance?
A: He brought down the house.

Q: Why didn't Samson like to argue with Delilah?
A: He didn't want to split hairs.

HIDDEN RUTH

The following nonsense paragraph hides ten words or names associated with Ruth. See if you can find them. (Note: Words and names are strung between the words of the story.)

Anna ominously looked at her image from a radically different angle and adjusted her feather boa, zebra-skin coat, and designer shades. From this angle, a very fashionable woman looked back. "Who loves you, baby?" she said. "I know ma or pa have to, and I know I do." With that, as if in slo-mo, a bug landed on her nose. *With reshaping,* she thought, *even my nose could be among those that are deemed fashionable.*

Here's what you're looking for:

Boaz	Naomi
Glean	Orpah
Leave	Redeem
Mara	Thresh
Moab	Widow

TV LISTINGS

Cable
The Weather Channel
Record-setting rain for the fortieth day!

Soap Opera
All My Children
Jacob loves Rachel, but Leah's bearing his children. The older sons are jealous of young Joseph. Will Rachel survive the birth of her second child?

Movie of the Week
Framed!
A loyal servant is falsely accused and tossed into prison. His dreams are his only hope for escape.

Soap Opera
The Young and the Grainless
About to be reunited with his brothers, Joseph wonders whether to trust them. He can't quite forget how they double-crossed him years earlier. Will they pass his test of loyalty?

Sitcom
Sinai-feld
The hilarious antics of Moses' other brother and his wacky friends.

SOUND CLIP: "Why are there *Ten* Commandments? Why not nine or seventeen? And what's the deal with coveting?"

Movie of the Week
The Spies Who Saved Me
Poignant tale of a bad girl gone good, who takes a chance on two dashing Israelite spies. See what happens when her world falls down around her and her life hangs by a thread.

2B
kings & things

(1 SAMUEL—ESTHER)

QUIZ 2B—1

1. **When the Israelites demanded a king, how did Samuel respond?**
    a. He warned against it.
    b. He wanted to be their first king.
    c. He wrote a new constitution.
    d. He went on strike.

2. **Which Israelite king was described as "head and shoulders taller than anyone else in the land" (1 Sam. 9:2)?**
    a. Samson
    b. Saul
    c. Hezekiah
    d. Dandruff

3. **Which of the following was *not* the father of a king of Israel?**
    a. David
    b. Kish
    c. Samuel
    d. Jesse

4. **To whom was it said? "People judge by outward appearance, but the Lord looks at a person's thoughts and intentions" (1 Sam. 16:7).**
    a. Samuel
    b. Solomon
    c. Esther
    d. The Spice Girls

5. **What ritual designated someone king of Israel?**
    a. Trumpets announced his entry into the Great Hall.
    b. He wore sackcloth and ashes for one day.
    c. A prophet poured oil on his head.
    d. He wore a T-shirt that said "I'm King."

6. **Michal was Saul's daughter. Who was her husband?**
   a. Jonathan
   b. David
   c. Barnabas
   d. Hank

7. **What prince warned David of Saul's attempts to kill him?**
   a. Absalom
   b. Solomon
   c. Jonathan
   d. The Bible character formerly known as a prince

8. **What future king did Abigail help, over the objections of her rich husband, Nabal?**
   a. Saul
   b. David
   c. Asa
   d. Tut

9. **Why did Saul consult a medium?**
   a. He wanted to know how to find David.
   b. He wanted to know the battle plans of the Philistines.
   c. He wanted to talk with the spirit of Samuel.
   d. He wasn't big enough for the extra-large.

10. **A crippled boy named Mephibosheth (Meh-FIB-o-sheth) was the only remaining member of King Saul's family. How did King David treat him?**
    a. With kindness, as his own son
    b. With suspicion—he shipped him away so he wouldn't cause trouble.
    c. With vengeance—he had the boy killed.
    d. With ice cream

11. **Where was Bathsheba when David first saw her?**
    a. Praying in the temple
    b. Visiting the palace

c. Bathing on her roof

d. Fighting in the army

12. Why did David have Bathsheba's husband, Uriah, killed?

a. He didn't like him.

b. To cover up the adultery David had committed

c. Uriah threatened David's life.

d. Because Bathsheba asked him to.

13. To whom was it said? "You are that man!" (2 Sam. 12:7).

a. Saul, anointed as king

b. David, accused of adultery and murder

c. Solomon, appointed to build the temple

d. Freddie, caught shoplifting

14. How did Absalom die?

a. He got his long hair caught in a tree and was found by enemy soldiers.

b. He shot himself with his own bow and arrow.

c. He tripped while mounting his horse and was trampled.

d. Old age

15. To whom was it said? "Because you have asked for wisdom in governing my people and have not asked for a long life or riches . . . I will give you what you asked for!" (1 Kings 3:11-12).

a. David

b. Solomon

c. Simon Peter

d. The queen of Sheba

16. What Israelite king did the queen of Sheba visit?

a. Saul

b. Ahab

c. Solomon

d. The king of Sheba

17. **King Rehoboam followed harsh policies that resulted in a rebellion that split his kingdom in two. Who was Rehoboam's father (and predecessor)?**
    a. Saul
    b. Solomon
    c. Jeroboam
    d. Rehoboam I

18. **Who led the revolt that split Israel into two kingdoms after Solomon's rule?**
    a. Joash
    b. John the Baptist
    c. Jeroboam
    d. Jerry Lewis

19. **Which of the following were kings of Israel?**
    a. Mordecai, Lazarus, Abner
    b. Jeroboam, Menahem, Hoshea
    c. Joash, Joab, Jonadab
    d. Frazier, Bradley, DeBusschre

20. **Which of the following were kings of Judah?**
    a. Zacchaeus, Zerubbabel, Zimri
    b. Belshazzar, Tiglath-Pileser, Cyrus
    c. Jotham, Ahaz, Asa
    d. Agnew, Mondale, Quayle

YOU SAW IT HERE FIRST

Insanity Defense

David, on the run from King Saul, ran into the grips of his (and Saul's) worst enemies: the Philistines. But he shrewdly saved himself by pretending to be crazy—scratching on doors and drooling. When David was hauled before the Philistine king, the king shrugged it off, saying, "Must you bring me a madman? We already have enough of them around here!" (1 Sam. 21:12-15).

Pop Song

There's lots of singing in Scripture, but the closest we come to a modern smash hit is a song sung about the military exploits of Saul and David: "Saul has killed his thousands, and David his ten thousands" (1 Sam. 18:7). The Bible says, "Women came out from all the towns along the way to celebrate . . . and they danced for joy with tambourines and cymbals" (1 Sam. 18:6). Sounds a lot like MTV.

CRAZY ADS

Tabloid
National Inspirer
"I Did It": King confesses adultery and murderous cover-up. Prophet Nathan gets an exclusive story.

Product
Bathsheba Hot Tubs
Specializing in rooftop installation

Product
Absalom Brand Hair Conditioner
For a princely shine
(Soon we'll be branching out into a line of untangling cream rinse.)

Web Site
www.temple.com
Follow the progress of temple construction. When will Hiram's next lumber shipment arrive? Are we getting more gold from Ophir?

Dumb Jokes

Q: Why did proud King Saul insist on making a sacrifice?
A: His altar ego

Q: What did King David's dog say to his master when he first saw Bathsheba?
A: Roof, roof!

Q: How was Absalom's behavior toward his father, King David?
A: Revolting

QUIZ 2B—2

1. **Who said it? "As surely as the Lord, the God of Israel, lives—the God whom I worship and serve—there will be no dew or rain during the next few years unless I give the word!" (1 Kings 17:1).**
   a. Aaron
   b. Joshua
   c. Elijah
   d. Willard Scott

2. **What superpower nation defeated the northern kingdom of Israel and relocated its people?**
   a. Aramea
   b. Assyria
   c. Egypt
   d. Afghanistan

3. **What king of Judah was besieged by Assyrian troops, prayed, and had a miraculous deliverance?**
   a. Solomon
   b. Ahab
   c. Hezekiah
   d. Haggai

4. **During a famine, Elijah camped by Kerith Brook and drank its water. How did he get bread and meat?**
   a. He stole from people's houses.
   b. Ravens brought it to him.
   c. It miraculously appeared on the ground each morning.
   d. 7-11

5. **While Elijah was staying with the widow of Zarephath, her son got sick and died. What did Elijah do?**
   a. Left the home
   b. Buried the boy in the plot he had picked for himself
   c. Raised the boy back to life
   d. Stopped eating her food

6. **On Mount Carmel, Elijah went up against 450 prophets of Baal. What was the competition?**
   a. Calling fire from heaven to consume their sacrifice
   b. Making it rain
   c. Building an altar the fastest
   d. Guessing which card Ahab was holding

7. **How did Elijah make his sacrifice even more difficult for fire to consume?**
   a. He built the altar of juniper wood rather than oak.
   b. He dug a trench around the altar and poured water over everything.
   c. He built the altar in a cave.
   d. He put up No Smoking signs.

8. **Camped out at Mount Sinai (Horeb), Elijah witnessed several natural wonders. In which of them did the Lord speak to him?**
   a. Earthquake
   b. Fire
   c. Windstorm
   d. Gentle whisper

9. **What did King Ahab want that belonged to a neighbor named Naboth?**
   a. A young lamb
   b. A vineyard
   c. A silver cup
   d. The patent for his new fire extinguisher

10. How did Jezebel get this for her husband?

a. She trumped up charges against Naboth and had him
stoned to death.

b. She had Naboth drafted into the army.

c. She took Naboth to court and bribed the judge.

d. She sweet-talked Naboth into donating it to the king's
scholarship fund.

11. How did Elisha purify some poisonous stew?

a. He threw some flour in.

b. He killed a young goat and boiled its forelegs.

c. He assembled a group of prophets to pray for the food.

d. He threw it out and took everyone to KFC.

**12. Elisha miraculously gave one needy woman an unending
supply of olive oil. What did she do with it?**

a. Made cakes for her family

b. Made bread for those who were even needier

c. Took a jar of oil to the temple

d. Sold the oil to pay her debts

**13. What prophet brought the son of the Shunemite woman
back to life?**

a. Elisha

b. Isaiah

c. Jeremiah

d. Heimlich

14. Why was Elisha's servant, Gehazi, stricken with leprosy?

a. He failed to salute Naaman, the Aramean commander.

b. He asked Naaman to pay for the healing and took the
payment as his own.

c. He tried to heal Naaman on his own.

d. He ate too much chocolate.

15. **When Elisha threw a stick into the river, what floated to the surface?**
    a. The stick
    b. An ax head that had fallen into the river
    c. All the fish in that section of the river
    d. Naaman's body

16. **The Assyrians' siege of Jerusalem was broken when . . .**
    a. the Egyptian army attacked them from the rear, killing 55,000 Assyrians.
    b. Jewish militias launched surprise night attacks on their camps, slaying 100,000.
    c. the angel of the Lord killed 185,000 Assyrian soldiers.
    d. they got bored and went home.

17. **Two kings of Judah were mere children when they took the throne, just seven and eight years old. Who were they?**
    a. Hezekiah and Jeremiah
    b. Ahab and Ahasuerus
    c. Joash and Josiah
    d. Jody and Buffy

18. **During the restoration of the temple under King Josiah, the high priest found something. What was it?**
    a. The Book of the Law
    b. Instructions from Josiah's long-dead father
    c. The ark of the covenant
    d. His missing skateboard

19. **Which of the following were gods worshiped by Israel's neighbors—and sometimes by the Israelites themselves?**
    a. Nehru, Gogol, and Mordock
    b. Baal, Chemosh, and Molech
    c. Gath, Zadok, and Gaza
    d. Sosa, McGwire, and Griffey

20. What nation's army destroyed the temple in Jerusalem about 586 B.C.?
   a. Assyria
   b. Babylon
   c. Persia
   d. Turkey

YOU SAW IT HERE FIRST

Cosmetics

Eyeliner, lipstick, blush—there's nothing new about makeup. Women have been painting their faces for millennia. Scripture notes that Jezebel "painted her eyelids and fixed her hair" as she watched the approach of the avenger who would kill her (2 Kings 9:30).

Water Works

Water supply is important for any community, and we often see water towers dotting the terrain in various towns. This was especially important in the arid climate of the Mideast. The Bible mentions several water-supply projects. The "pool of Gibeon" was one of the earliest, and it seems to have been a kind of landmark in its area (2 Sam. 2:13; Jer. 41:12). Under siege by the Assyrians, King Hezekiah constructed a tunnel that would ensure Jerusalem's water supply. In 2 Kings 20:20, this is noted as one of his great achievements.

CRAZY ADS

WWF Poster
Clash for the Kingdom!
Jeroboam vs. Rehoboam
   The Ephraim Avenger meets the Prince of Pieces
   Will the Son of Sol tear this raging rebel to pieces?
   Or will the Sheik of Shechem wreck 'im?
   Ten tribes to two, but Reho has the dynasty

Product
Naaman Brand Bath Oil
   So you never have to dip in the muddy Jordan again

Dumb Jokes

Q: What judgment did King Solomon hand down with the two woman claiming one baby?
A: It was a split decision.

Q: What did Elisha say when they wanted him to find the hatchet that fell in the river?
A: Don't ax me!

HIDDEN ELIJAH

The following nonsense story hides ten words or names associated with Elijah. Can you find them? (Note: Words and names are strung between the words of the story.)

It's a brave new world, the sales rep said as he drove through Cuba. Along the way, he was pleased with his new car, mellowly grooving on the local jazz, a rep hat hanging low on his brow (as a haberdasher once taught him). When the car came to a halt, a rebellious group surrounded him. *If I represent my products well,* he thought, *who rebels? Let them watch. A riot, I feel, is hardly the worst that could happen.*

Here's what you're looking for:

Ahab	Elisha
Altar	Fire
Baal	Horeb
Carmel	Raven
Chariot	Zarephath

QUIZ 2B–3

1. What Babylonian king led the destruction of Jerusalem?
   a. Pharaoh
   b. Nebuchadnezzar
   c. Hezekiah
   d. Belshazzar

2. **What measured thirty feet by thirty feet and was fifteen feet high?**
   a. Noah's ark
   b. The ark of the covenant
   c. The altar in Solomon's temple
   d. Goliath's apartment

3. **To whom was it said? "Then if my people who are called by my name will humble themselves and pray and seek my face and turn from their wicked ways, I will hear from heaven and will forgive their sins and heal their land" (2 Chron. 7:14).**
   a. Joshua
   b. Solomon
   c. Ezekiel
   d. Simon Peter

4. **Who had 12,000 horses (2 Chron. 11:25)?**
   a. Moses
   b. Joseph
   c. Solomon
   d. Marco Polo

5. **King Hezekiah threw a Passover celebration in Jerusalem. Besides his own people, who was invited?**
   a. His enemies, the Assyrians
   b. The people of the northern kingdom of Israel
   c. The queen of Sheba
   d. Anyone who came in costume

6. **What Persian king allowed the Jews to return to their homeland?**
   a. Darius
   b. Cyrus
   c. Belshazzar
   d. Aladdin

7. **Zerubbabel was a leader of what project?**
   a. The return from captivity and rebuilding of the temple
   b. The instruction of God's people in the law
   c. The construction of Nebuchadnezzar's image
   d. The removal of the letter Z from all world alphabets

8. **Who said it? "I have zealously served the Lord God Almighty. But the people of Israel have broken their covenant with you, torn down your altars, and killed every one of your prophets. I alone am left, and now they are trying to kill me, too" (1 Kings 19:10).**
   a. David
   b. Elisha
   c. Elijah
   d. Pontius Pilate

9. **What did Elisha do to some boys who were mocking him?**
   a. He spoke God's Word and converted them.
   b. He called lightning from heaven to strike them dead.
   c. He returned them to their parents for discipline.
   d. He called bears out of the woods to maul them.

10. **What did the mocking boys call Elisha?**
    a. Prophet of doom
    b. Old Know-nothing
    c. Baldhead
    d. Scooter

11. **Zerubbabel and Jeshua were leaders of the people who returned after the Babylonian Captivity. Who were the main prophets at that time (Ezra 5:1)?**
    a. Haggai and Zechariah
    b. Isaiah and Hezekiah
    c. Ezra and Ezion-Geber
    d. Cagney and Lacey

12. **Who wrote this? "Praise the Lord, the God of our ancestors, who made the king want to beautify the Temple of the Lord in Jerusalem! And praise him for demonstrating such unfailing love to me by honoring me before the king, his council, and all his mighty princes!"**
    a. David
    b. Asaph
    c. Ezra
    d. Paul

13. **Who was opposed in his building project by Sanballat, Tobiah, and Geshem the Arab?**
    a. Solomon
    b. Nehemiah
    c. Herod
    d. Bob Vila

14. **What construction project included the Sheep Gate, the Fish Gate, and the Dung Gate?**
    a. Herod's palace at Caesarea
    b. The Tower of Babel
    c. The wall of Jerusalem
    d. Disney World

15. **Who succeeded Vashti as queen of Persia?**
    a. Ruth
    b. Esther
    c. Jezebel
    d. Cleopatra

16. **What had Queen Vashti done to displease King Xerxes?**
    a. She criticized him in public.
    b. She had an affair with his prime minister.
    c. She wouldn't come when he called.
    d. At a royal banquet, she belched.

17. How did Esther save the Jews from annihilation?
a. Poisoned Haman, who was plotting to kill her people
b. Asked the king to spare her people
c. Planned a rebellion against the Persian authorities
d. Hid them in the palace basement

18. Who replaced Haman as prime minister?
a. Mordecai
b. Esther
c. Daniel
d. Howard

19. What is the proper order of these three books of the Bible?
a. Ezra, Nehemiah, Esther
b. Esther, Nehemiah, Ezra
c. Esther, Ezra, Nehemiah
d. Nehemiah, Ezra, Better Than Ezra

20. Today Jews still observe an annual festival celebrating the way Esther and Mordecai saved their people. This is known as . . .
a. Passover
b. Purim
c. Penitence
d. Daylight Savings Time

AMAZING FACTS

The Old Testament refers to a number of other history books that were available back then. Some of their contents may now be included in Old Testament history, but most of it is probably lost to us. The missing books include:

• *The Book of the Wars of the Lord* (Num. 21:14)
• *The Book of Jashar* (Josh. 10:13)
• *The Record of Nathan the Prophet* (1 Chron. 29:29)
• *The Record of Gad the Seer* (1 Chron. 29:29)
• *The Record of Samuel the Seer* (1 Chron. 29:29)

- *The Prophecy of Ahijah from Shiloh* (2 Chron. 9:29)
- *The Visions of Iddo the Seer* (2 Chron. 9:29)
- *The Record of Shemaiah the Prophet* (2 Chron. 12:15)
- *The Commentary of Iddo the Prophet* (2 Chron. 13:22)
- *The Record of Jehu Son of Hanani* (2 Chron. 20:34)

CRAZY ADS

Movie
Chariots of Fire
    Starring Elisha Gehazi
    Special appearance by Ben Hadad
    Enemies all around you? Who's around *them?*
    Music by Evangelist, in SurroundSound
    "Open your eyes and see this film sensation!"

Magazine
Young Miss
- Cover Girl Esther: A Beauty with Brains
- How to Keep Your King and Save Your Race
- How to Handle Gallows Humor
- When the Prime Minister Is Sinister
- Advice Column by Cousin Mord

Dumb Jokes

Q: How did King Xerxes feel when he realized Haman wanted to
    kill a man who had saved his life?
A: Mordecai-ed

HIDDEN ESTHER

The following nonsense story hides fourteen words or names associated with Esther. Can you find them? (Note: Words and names are
strung between the words of the story.)

"Ham and cheese make a unique enchilada for lunches or suppers,"
I announced as I folded up a lace tablecloth. In the gym next door,
made creepy by its bouts, Boxer X established supremacy. Watching

a television at the gym, he says, "She don't let me watch no shows, 'cept ER." Caitlin, his wife, a star in her own right, plunged to new legal lows as she tried to interest her beau, typing his medical records: "Blood Type O." Please stop him, or de-Caitlin his career.

Here's what you're looking for:

Beauty	Mordecai
Decree	Palace
Esther	People
Feast	Persia
Gallows	Queen
Gate	Scepter
Haman	Xerxes

TV LISTINGS

Drama
The Incredible Hulk
See the adventures of Goliath of Gath as he torments young shepherds.

Soap Opera
Dynasty
Amnon is heartsick over his half-sis Tamar. But will his attack bring vengeance from Absalom? Then see how a brooding father, King David, handles the violence in his own home. Meanwhile, the descendants of Saul plot to grab the kingdom back. Will Solomon be the king's successor?

Drama
The X-Files
Xerxes discovers that agent Mordecai has thwarted a plot against the king's life.

2C
the write stuff

(JOB – MALACHI)

QUIZ 2C—1

1. Who (at one time) had seven sons, three daughters, 7000 sheep, 3000 camels, 500 teams of oxen, 500 donkeys, and many servants?
   a. Solomon
   b. The queen of Sheba
   c. Job
   d. Bill Gates

2. Who said it? "I came naked from my mother's womb, and I will be stripped of everything when I die. The Lord gave me everything I had, and the Lord has taken it away. Praise the name of the Lord!"
   a. Adam
   b. Eve
   c. Job
   d. Delilah

3. Who told Job to "curse God and die"?
   a. Bildad the Shuhite
   b. Satan
   c. Elihu
   d. His wife

4. Which of the following creatures are *not* mentioned by God in the book of Job?
   a. Mountain goats
   b. The ostrich
   c. The hippopotamus
   d. Buffalo

5. Besides David, who wrote the most psalms?
   a. Asaph
   b. Aaron
   c. Samuel
   d. Selah

6. **In Psalm 19:14, what does the psalmist want to be "pleasing" to the Lord?**

    a. The words of his mouth and the thoughts of his heart

    b. The actions of his life

    c. The sacrifices he brings and the prayers he offers

    d. His appearance

7. **Finish this verse: "The Lord is my light and my salvation . . ." (Psalm 27:1, NIV)**

    a. my rest when I am weary.

    b. a very present help in trouble.

    c. whom shall I fear?

    d. and I sure need it!

8. **Finish this verse: "Taste and see . . ." (Psalm 34:8)**

    a. that the Lord is good.

    b. the wine of righteousness.

    c. the glory of the one who loves you.

    d. these incredible nachos.

9. **Finish this verse: "God is our refuge and strength . . ." (Psalm 46:1, NIV)**

    a. he protects me in times of woe.

    b. an ever-present help in trouble.

    c. my tower of power against my foes.

    d. and I am just a refugee.

10. **Psalm 51 begins "Have mercy on me, O God, because of your unfailing love." When did David write it?**

    a. As he fled from King Saul

    b. After slaying Goliath

    c. After he had committed adultery

    d. On a weekend vacation to the Mediterranean

11. **Finish this verse: "Create in me a clean heart, O God. . ." (Psalm 51:10)**

    a. Make me clean as a well-swept floor.

    b. Renew a right spirit within me.

c. For I devote my heart to you forever.

d. For the one I've got is pretty filthy.

12. **Finish this verse: "He who dwells in the shelter of the Most High will . . ." (Psalm 91:1, NIV)**

a. live in peace and harmony.

b. rest in the shadow of the Almighty.

c. honor the Lord all the days of his life.

d. never need an umbrella.

13. **According to the first verses of Psalms 96 and 98, what should we sing to the Lord?**

a. A new song

b. A melody that springs from the heart

c. A song with many instruments

d. "Kum Ba Yah"

14. **According to Psalm 118:22, what has happened to "the stone rejected by the builders"?**

a. It was returned to the scrap heap.

b. It fell upon evildoers.

c. It became the cornerstone.

d. It invented rock music.

15. **Finish this verse: "Unless the Lord builds a house . . ." (Psalm 127:1)**

a. it will fall into the ashes.

b. there will be no joy in it.

c. the work of the builders is useless.

d. you won't get much of a mortgage rate.

16. **According to Psalm 137, where was it that "we sat and wept . . . put away our lyres, hanging them on the branches of the willow trees"?**

a. in slavery in Egypt

b. beside the rivers of Babylon

c. in the Garden of Eden

d. Wrigley Field

17. **Which of the following is *not* mentioned in Psalm 139 as something God knows?**
    a. When I sit down or stand up
    b. My every thought
    c. The sin hidden deep in my heart
    d. What I am going to say even before I say it

18. **According to Psalm 139:13, where did God "knit me together"?**
    a. In your perfect mind
    b. In my mother's womb
    c. In the time before time
    d. In crocheting class

19. **In Psalm 145, who is described as "kind and merciful, slow to get angry"?**
    a. David
    b. Moses
    c. The blessed man
    d. The Lord

20. **What phrase begins and ends the last five psalms?**
    a. Let it be so! (Amen!)
    b. Praise the Lord! (Hallelujah!)
    c. I call out to you, O Lord!
    d. We're almost finished now!

YOU SAW IT HERE FIRST

Love Song

The Song of Songs is a beautiful love song. Some have seen it as an allegory of the love between Christ and the church or between God and Israel, but it's also great romance.

CRAZY ADS

Calendar
The "Time for Everything" Calendar

All right, *when* is it a time to mourn and *when* should we dance? This helpful calendar (with its companion appointment book) tells you exactly when to carry on all these activities. No more guesswork. Because you don't want to be scattering stones when it's time to gather stones together.

Product
Song of Songs Lip Balm

So your kisses will be sweeter than wine

Dumb Jokes

God asked Satan why he was loafing. "Temptation is just too easy," the devil replied. "There are no challenges anymore."

God said, "Get a Job!"

MINI-QUIZ: PROVERBS

Match the start of each proverb with its ending.

1. Can a man scoop fire into his lap . . .

a. is like a gold ring in a pig's snout.

2. People who wink at wrong trouble, . . .

b. Don't eat too much of cause it, or it will make you sick!

3. A woman who is beautiful but lacks discretion . . .

c. is as dangerous as a thornbush brandished by a drunkard.

4. Some who are poor pretend to be rich; . . .

d. then brags about getting a bargain!

5. The buyer haggles over the price, saying, "It's worthless," . . .

e. and not be burned?

6. Do you like honey? . . .

f. others who are rich pretend to be poor.

7. If your enemies are hungry, give them food to eat. If they are thirsty, give them water to drink. . . .

g. it will be counted as a curse!

8. A proverb in a fool's mouth . . .

h. but a bold reproof promotes peace.

9. Just as damaging as a mad man shooting a lethal weapon . . .

i. is someone who lies to a friend and then says, "I was only joking."

10. If you shout a pleasant greeting to your neighbor too early in the morning, . . .

j. You will heap burning coals on their heads, and the Lord will reward you.

QUIZ 2C–2

1. **What insect is mentioned in Proverbs as an example of a hard worker (6:6)?**
   a. The grasshopper
   b. The mosquito
   c. The ant
   d. The leech

2. **Fill in the blank: "Wounds from a friend can be _____" (Prov. 27:6, NIV).**
   a. deadly
   b. unexpected
   c. trusted
   d. a good way to ruin a friendship

3. **Which of the following is listed as an activity of "the virtuous wife" in Proverbs 31?**
   a. She invests her family's money wisely.
   b. She quilts her own bedspreads.
   c. She keeps up on all the neighborhood events.
   d. She launches her own Internet business.

4. **The author of Ecclesiastes tries a number of pursuits, finding them all meaningless. Which of the following is *not* somewhere he tries to find meaning?**
   a. Work
   b. Companionship
   c. Food
   d. Power

5. **Which of the following is *not* some of the lovers' conversation in Song of Songs?**
   a. Your hair falls in waves, like a flock of goats frisking down the slopes of Gilead.
   b. Your nose is a proud watchtower over your face, like the turret of David.
   c. Your teeth are as white as sheep, newly shorn and washed.
   d. Your cheeks behind your veil are like pomegranate halves—lovely and delicious.

6. **Fill in the blank: "Many waters cannot quench _____; neither can rivers drown it" (Song 8:7).**
   a. my heart
   b. love
   c. the fires of passion
   d. my raging thirst

7. **When Isaiah was called to be a prophet, he had a vision of the Lord in the temple. Who was singing, "Holy, holy, holy" (Isa. 6)?**
   a. Isaiah
   b. Angels with six wings
   c. Beasts and elders
   d. Bebe and Cece Winans

8. **Fill in the blank: "The grass withers, and the flowers fade, but _____ stands forever" (Isa. 40:8).**
   a. God's eternal love
   b. the word of our God

c. the sin of your heart

d. superglue

9. **Isaiah 42 talks about someone special. "He is my chosen one, and I am pleased with him. I have put my Spirit upon him." What term is used for this person?**

a. The Servant

b. The Savior

c. The Rock

d. Immanuel

10. **What bad-news prophet did the men of Anathoth want to kill?**

a. Nathan

b. Elijah

c. Jeremiah

d. John the Baptist

11. **Who said it? "Can you shout to the clouds and make it rain? Can you make lightning appear and cause it to strike as you direct it? Who gives intuition and instinct? Who is wise enough to count all the clouds? Who can tilt the water jars of heaven, turning the dry dust to clumps of mud?" (Job 38:34-38).**

a. Adam

b. God

c. Elijah

d. Job

12. **What did Jeremiah do after King Jehoiakim burned the scroll he had written?**

a. He wrote another.

b. He called down God's wrath upon the king.

c. He quit trying to get his message across.

d. He went on strike.

13. **Who was told to eat a scroll God gave him?**
    a. Moses
    b. Ezekiel
    c. Peter
    d. Elijah

14. **What did the scroll taste like?**
    a. Olives
    b. Mustard
    c. Honey
    d. Paper

15. **Ezekiel saw a valley filled with dry bones. Then what happened?**
    a. The bones began to connect and become living people.
    b. The bones disintegrated into nothing.
    c. The bones became weapons picked up by strange beasts.
    d. Ezekiel woke up feeling sore.

16. **According to Ezekiel, what would be 1½ miles long, with three gates, each named after a tribe of Israel?**
    a. The walls of Jericho
    b. The armies of Gog and Magog
    c. Each of the four walls of the new city of God
    d. Solomon's temple

17. **Who dieted on veggies and water for ten days and fared better than those who ate the king's rich food?**
    a. David and his mighty men
    b. Daniel and his three friends
    c. Delilah and the women of Philistia
    d. Jenny Craig

18. **King Nebuchadnezzar dreamed of a statue with a head of gold, chest of silver, thighs of bronze. What were its feet made of?**
    a. Flesh
    b. Straw
    c. Iron and clay
    d. Bunions

19. **What penalty did Daniel's friends face for not bowing to the king's gold statue?**
    a. A blazing furnace
    b. Hanging
    c. Life in prison
    d. Folk songs

20. **What was the meaning of the "writing on the wall" seen by King Belshazzar?**
    a. He would enjoy long life and prosperity.
    b. His kingdom would be conquered by the Medes and Persians.
    c. There was a traitor in his government.
    d. He needed new wallpaper.

AMAZING FACTS

The description "holier than thou" was originally used by Isaiah to describe the "obstinate" people who arrogantly reject the Lord (Isa. 65:5).

The phrase "a drop in the bucket" appeared first in Isaiah 40:15 to describe the nations surrounding Israel—compared to the Lord's power.

CRAZY ADS

Product

Ezekiel Athletic Ointment
For those dry bones

Dumb Jokes

Q: What Old Testament book must have been written by
shepherds?

A: Lamb-entations

QUIZ 2C–3

1. Why was Daniel thrown into the lions' den?
   a. He wouldn't stop praying, even when it was made illegal.
   b. He angered the king with his interpretation of a dream.
   c. He led a rebellion of Jews against the Persian authorities.
   d. He snuck into the king's pasture and tipped all the cows.

2. Gomer was the unfaithful wife of what prophet?
   a. Elijah
   b. Amos
   c. Hosea
   d. John the Baptist

**3. The prophet Amos pulled no punches. He insulted the
Samaritan women who "oppress the poor and crush the
needy and are always asking your husbands for another
drink!" What did he call them (Amos 4:1)?**
   a. Hungry leeches
   b. Fat cows
   c. Wild donkeys
   d. Laughing hyenas

**4. Jonah got in trouble for going west toward Tarshish.
Where did God want him to go?**
   a. Jerusalem
   b. Nineveh
   c. Damascus
   d. Nirvana

5. What did Jonah do inside the fish?
   a. He prayed.
   b. He panicked.

c. He pounded.

d. He planned his funeral.

6. **When Jonah finally got to Nineveh, how did the people respond to his message?**

   a. They beat him up and threw him in jail.

   b. They repented of their sin.

   c. They wanted to hear more about his God.

   d. They thought he smelled like fish.

7. **How did Jonah react to the way Nineveh responded?**

   a. He quietly accepted the will of God.

   b. He resolved to keep preaching, despite all the obstacles.

   c. He was angry that God let such a wicked city repent.

   d. He longed for the good old days with the fish.

8. **What does the prophet Micah say about the little town of Bethlehem (Mic. 5:2)?**

   a. There will be a special star shining upon it.

   b. It is the hometown of David.

   c. A great ruler will come from Bethlehem.

   d. It could use more hotel rooms.

9. **Finish this verse: "The Lord is good. When trouble comes . . ." (Nah. 1:7)**

   a. he is a strong refuge.

   b. he provides righteousness.

   c. we flee to his holy temple.

   d. we can pretend it isn't there.

10. **What Old Testament prophet said he would climb into his watchtower and wait for the Lord's answer to his complaint?**

    a. David

    b. Habakkuk

    c. Agabus

    d. John the Baptist

11. **A man named Baruch worked as a secretary for what prophet?**
    a. Elisha
    b. Zechariah
    c. Jeremiah
    d. Kelly

12. **Fill in the blank: "Walk _____ and do what is right" (Zeph. 2:3).**
    a. carefully
    b. quickly
    c. on the left
    d. humbly

13. **Fill in the blank: "Take courage and _____, for I am with you, says the Lord Almighty" (Hag. 2:4).**
    a. pray
    b. work
    c. sing
    d. form a committee

14. **Fill in the blank: "It is not by force nor by strength, but by _____, says the Lord Almighty" (Zech. 4:6).**
    a. my Spirit
    b. clever planning
    c. creativity
    d. meditation

15. **According to Malachi 2:16, how does God feel about divorce?**
    a. He hates it.
    b. He doesn't care much about it.
    c. He excludes divorced people from his kingdom.
    d. He understands it when love is no longer there.

16. **Malachi predicts the return of another prophet "before that great and dreadful day of the Lord arrives" (Mal. 4:5). What does he call him?**
    a. The truth-teller
    b. Elijah
    c. The Baptizer
    d. That prophet guy

17. **Who said it? "Look! . . . I see four men, unbound, walking around in the fire. They aren't even hurt by the flames! And the fourth looks like a divine being!" (Dan. 3:25).**
    a. Jeremiah
    b. Daniel
    c. King Nebuchadnezzar
    d. Smokey the Bear

18. **Which prophet saw a vision of wheels within wheels?**
    a. Job
    b. Ezekiel
    c. Amos
    d. Henry Ford

19. **What does the book of Lamentations lament?**
    a. The decline in morality of the northern kingdom of Israel
    b. The destruction of Jerusalem by the Babylonians
    c. The defeat of Elijah by the prophets of Baal
    d. The four hundredth straight losing season of the Ephraim Expos

20. **What once-soggy prophet complained when God allowed a worm to eat a plant that was giving him shade?**
    a. Isaiah
    b. Micah
    c. Jonah
    d. John the Baptist

YOU SAW IT HERE FIRST

Performance Art

Nowadays people do all sorts of crazy things in the name of art—smearing themselves with chocolate or wrapping a building in fabric. But that's nothing new. In ancient Babylon, the Jewish prophet Ezekiel often made statements with odd antics—following God's instructions the whole time. Once he lay on his left side for more than a year, then rolled over and lay on his right side for forty more days—symbolizing the sin of God's people (Ezek. 4:4-6). Then he shaved his hair and beard off and scattered a third of the hair to the winds, beating another third with a sword—all to show what would happen to God's people (Ezek. 5:1-3). And there was other strange stuff too, but nothing with chocolate.

Skin Lotion

The area of Gilead, just east of the Jordan River, was known for a healing balm. Jeremiah mentions that lotion, but then mourns that there is "no healing for the wounds of my people" (Jer. 8:22).

Dumb Jokes

Q: What did King Nebuchadnezzar do to Shadrach, Meshach, and Abednego when they wouldn't bow down to him?
A: He had them fired.

Q: What did it prove when Daniel came out of the lion's den alive?
A: That when he talked about God, he wasn't lion.

HIDDEN PROPHETS

The names of all twelve minor prophets (and two major ones) are hidden in the following silly story. Can you find them? (Note: Three names were impossible to hide fully, so we went with abbreviations for Habakkuk, Zephaniah, and Zechariah—Hab., Zeph., and Zech.)

I have to give that comic a hand. He spoke on a human level, making the ordinary Joe laugh out loud. I've never known one whose attitude was such a blessing, especially when he mentioned his prize Chia Pet, which looked like the head of Michael Jordan. I elbowed my wife, Gail, and laughed out loud. He made it sound normal—a Chia Pet that spilled, turning his carpeting to shag. Gail and I howled. Too bad I—ah—was distracted, shall we say, by the mustard. I had a nice-size Philly cheese steak with spicy Dijon. A hot dog would make me sneeze, kielbasa is OK, but this was a most delicious treat.

Here's what you're looking for:

Ezekiel	Micah
Daniel	Nahum
Hosea	Hab.
Joel	Zeph.
Amos	Haggai
Obadiah	Zech.
Jonah	Malachi

TV LISTINGS

Sitcom
I Dream of Danny
> Our hero lands in a Persian court, interpreting dreams for a variety of masters. This week: He decodes some strange graffiti.

Sitcom
Different Spokes
The prophet Ezekiel keeps seeing wheels within wheels . . . and otherworldly creatures.

2D
good news
(MATTHEW – JOHN)

QUIZ 2D—1

1. **How did the angel of the Lord tell Joseph to marry Mary?**
   a. Through Zechariah the prophet
   b. In a dream
   c. He approached Joseph in his carpentry shop.
   d. FedEx

2. **Who was king of Israel at the time Jesus was born?**
   a. Herod
   b. Pontius Pilate
   c. Nero
   d. Hezekiah

3. **Zechariah had a problem when he came out of the temple after meeting with the angel. What was it?**
   a. He was limping.
   b. He could not speak.
   c. He was shining like the sun.
   d. He'd forgotten how to tie his sandals.

4. **Who was Zechariah's wife?**
   a. Mary
   b. Martha
   c. Elizabeth
   d. Mrs. Zechariah

5. **What did the shepherds do when they heard the news of Jesus' birth?**
   a. They prayed together.
   b. They tried to comfort their dazed sheep.
   c. They hurried to Bethlehem to see for themselves.
   d. They scraped up money to buy gold, frankincense, and myrrh.

6. **What general area were the wise men from?**
   a. Eastern lands
   b. Western highlands

c. Southern deserts

d. Northern countries

7. Where did Mary, Joseph, and Jesus live when they left Egypt?

a. Nazareth

b. Bethlehem

c. Capernaum

d. The Riviera

8. How old was Jesus when his parents found him among the teachers of the temple courts, listening to them and asking questions?

a. Two

b. Twelve

c. Thirty

d. Eighty-three

9. How old was Jesus when he began his public ministry?

a. About twelve

b. Eighteen

c. About thirty

d. As old as the fig tree his mother planted

10. What were John the Baptist's clothes made of?

a. Suede

b. Camel hair and leather

c. Fine linen

d. The skin of an unspotted lamb

11. What foods were John the Baptist's favorites?

a. Wine and bread

b. Grapes and new-picked figs

c. Locusts and wild honey

d. peanut butter and jelly

12. **John the Baptist baptized with water. What did he say Jesus (the one coming after him) would baptize with?**
   a. The Holy Spirit and fire
   b. Fire and ice
   c. The conviction of sin and fiery judgment
   d. A fire hose

13. **According to Matthew 4:1, why did the Holy Spirit lead Jesus out to the wilderness?**
   a. To show him the ways of men
   b. To meet the Essene hermits
   c. To be tempted by the devil
   d. To see if he could find his way back

14. **Jesus said, "Man does not live on bread alone" (NIV) but on what?**
   a. Holiness and humility
   b. Every word that comes from the mouth of God
   c. Companionship
   d. The four basic food groups

15. **Instead of praying on the street corners like the hypocrites do, where did Jesus say we should go to pray?**
   a. The temple
   b. A mountaintop
   c. Away by yourself, with the door closed
   d. The nearest TV studio

16. **Who was Jesus talking about when he said we cannot serve two masters?**
   a. God and money
   b. The church and Satan
   c. Our own desires and the ways of the Lord
   d. Republicans and Democrats

17. "They don't need to plant or harvest or put food in barns because your heavenly Father feeds them" (Matt. 6:26). Who was Jesus talking about?

   a. Beggars

   b. His disciples

   c. Prophets

   d. Birds

18. If you throw pearls to pigs, what will happen?

   a. They'll eat them.

   b. The pigs will become holy.

   c. They will trample them.

   d. The pigs will look a lot more elegant, but a bit old-fashioned.

19. How does Jesus sum up the Law and the Prophets?

   a. Don't do things that displease God.

   b. Help everyone who is truly in need.

   c. Do unto others as you would have them do unto you.

   d. The Law gets two stars, the Prophets three stars.

20. What illness was Peter's mother-in-law stricken with before Jesus healed her?

   a. A fever

   b. A bleeding disease

   c. Leprosy

   d. She was demon-possessed, at least that's what Peter said.

AMAZING FACTS

At the beginning of Matthew's Gospel, he lists the family tree of Jesus. Only four women are included in that list before Mary. Two of them (Rahab and Ruth) were foreigners (and Rahab was a prostitute). The other two were involved in sexual scandals—Tamar with Judah and Bathsheba with David. Was Matthew trying to blunt, the criticism from those who would be scandalized by the Virgin Mary conceiving out of wedlock?

CRAZY ADS

MILK CARTON
Missing
Prodigious child
Jesus of Nazareth
DOB: 12/25/4 B.C.
Last seen: In temple complex, Jerusalem

PRODUCT
Stoneman's Bread
Temptingly delicious

Dumb Jokes

Q: Where did the wise men go when they visited Disney World?
A: The Magi Kingdom.

Q: What rock song did the wise men sing as they traveled?
A: "Starway to Heaven"

Q: How did one wise man feel when he couldn't return his gift?
A: Incensed.

MINI-QUIZ: BEATITUDES
Match the blessed people with their blessings (Matt. 5:3-10, NIV).

1. Blessed are the poor in spirit
2. Blessed are those who mourn
3. Blessed are the meek
4. Blessed are those who hunger and thirst for righteousness
5. Blessed are the merciful
6. Blessed are the pure in heart
7. Blessed are the peacemakers

a. for they will inherit the earth
b. for they will see God
c. for theirs is the kingdom of heaven
d. for they will be filled
e. for they will be called sons of God.
f. for they will be comforted
g. for theirs is the kingdom of heaven

8. Blessed are those who are persecuted because of righteousness

h. for they will be shown mercy

QUIZ 2D—2

1. **Whom did the Pharisees say Jesus was using to drive out demons?**
    a. His Father
    b. The prince of demons
    c. The spirit of Elijah
    d. His chauffeur

2. **Who was Jesus pointing to when he said, "These are my mother and my brothers" (Matt. 12:49)?**
    a. His mother and brothers
    b. His disciples
    c. All the people of Judea
    d. The Pharisees

3. **What is the smallest of seeds, yet grows to be the largest of garden plants?**
    a. The mustard seed
    b. The watermelon seed
    c. The coriander seed
    d. The seed of contention

4. **What bread ingredient does Jesus compare with the kingdom of heaven?**
    a. Flour
    b. Butter
    c. Yeast
    d. Crust

5. What happens when one blind person guides another blind person?
a. Both fall into a ditch.
b. They step on one another's toes.
c. They understand each other more fully.
d. People around them offer assistance.

6. Who appeared with Jesus on the Mount of Transfiguration (Matt. 17:3)?
a. Andrew, James, and John
b. John the Baptist
c. Moses and Elijah
d. No one

7. What did Peter want to build on the mountain where Jesus was transfigured?
a. Three shrines or shelters
b. A replica of the ark of the covenant
c. Seven altars
d. A boat

8. Where did Peter get the coin to pay the taxes for Jesus and the disciples?
a. From the mouth of a fish
b. On the ground
c. From Andrew
d. From the money changers

9. What happens when two or three come together in Jesus' name?
a. They have a fight.
b. They have refreshments.
c. They have much power in prayer.
d. Jesus is there with them.

10. **Peter asked, "How often should I forgive someone who sins against me? Seven times?" (Matt. 18:21). What was Jesus' answer?**
    a. Yes
    b. Once is enough.
    c. Twice is plenty, unless he is your brother.
    d. Seventy times seven

11. **According to Jesus, "The Kingdom of Heaven belongs to such as these" (Matt. 19:14). Such as what?**
    a. Little children
    b. Tax collectors
    c. Baptized believers
    d. Banks

12. **A rich young man asked Jesus how to have eternal life. What did Jesus ultimately suggest (Matt. 19:16–22)?**
    a. Ask the Pharisees.
    b. Go and sell all you have.
    c. Study my words and teach them to others.
    d. Floss daily.

13. **When the Son of Man comes in glory, he will separate the nations like what two animals?**
    a. Dogs and cats
    b. Birds and fish
    c. Sheep and goats
    d. Worms and wombats

14. **What happened to the demons who were living in the two men in the land of the Gadarenes?**
    a. Jesus sent them into a herd of pigs.
    b. They afflicted many houses of that region.
    c. They were cast into the seventh circle of hell.
    d. They moved to the suburbs.

15. **Finish this saying: "Healthy people don't need a doctor— . . ." (Matt. 9:12).**
    a. they need forgiveness.
    b. sick people do.
    c. any more than tax collectors need money.
    d. doctors need healthy people.

16. **Jesus healed two blind men and sternly warned them to tell no one about it. What did the two do then?**
    a. They left the area so they wouldn't blurt out Jesus' secret.
    b. They reported Jesus' actions only to the rabbi.
    c. They became Jesus' disciples.
    d. They spread his fame all over the region.

17. **Who told Jesus that his disciples shouldn't be picking grain on the Sabbath?**
    a. The Pharisees
    b. The Roman centurion
    c. Judas Iscariot
    d. The farmer

18. **On what day did Jesus heal the man with a shriveled hand?**
    a. On his twentieth birthday
    b. On the Sabbath
    c. On the first day of his ministry
    d. Thanksgiving

19. **Jesus took three of his disciples with him as he prayed in the garden. Which ones?**
    a. Peter, James, and John
    b. Zacchaeus and the two sons of Zebedee
    c. Matthew, Mark, and Luke
    d. John the Baptist, John the Apostle, and Paul

20. **To whom was the Gospel of Luke written?**
    a. Luke
    b. Peter

c. Theophilus

d. Nero

THEMES OF THE GOSPELS

Each of the four Gospels—Matthew, Mark, Luke and John—has a distinctive quality. They tell many of the same stories but in different ways. Here's how to tell them apart.

Matthew—throws the welcome MAT out to THE Jews. This writer showed how Jesus was the fulfillment of the Jewish Scriptures.

Mark—spelled backwards is KRAM, and Mark's the shortest Gospel, cramming everything into sixteen chapters. It's probably also the earliest, as if Mark was cramming for a test, trying to get it all written before people forgot it.

Luke—was a careful historian. If he didn't know something, he'd LOOK it up. Many have doubted the details in Luke's writings, but archaeologists have consistently confirmed that he was right. You can look it up!

John—wanted people to JOIN the cause, so he records the many things Jesus said about himself (see John 20:30-31). If you want a friend to follow Jesus, give him or her the book of John.

MAT, KRAM, LOOK, and JOIN. That's not so hard to remember, is it?

CRAZY ADS

Web Site
www.beatitude.net
Test yourself! See how blessed you are!

Product
Faith's Mustard
Small seeds . . . big flavor

Business
HeartCare Health Insurance
Because healthy people don't need a doctor

QUIZ 2D–3

1. Who were the sons of Zebedee?
   a. Peter and Andrew
   b. James and John
   c. The scribes
   d. Cain and Abel

2. Who said it? "My son, your sins are forgiven" (Mark 2:5).
   a. Peter and John
   b. Jesus
   c. Joseph
   d. Caiaphas

3. How did the religious teachers respond to that last statement?
   a. They considered it blasphemy because only God can forgive sins.
   b. They basically agreed, but wished the statement wasn't so blunt.
   c. They wanted forgiveness for themselves.
   d. They didn't hear it because of the crowd's commotion.

4. According to Jesus, what does new wine need?
   a. Joyful drinkers
   b. Time to settle
   c. New wineskins
   d. Wedding receptions

5. In the parable of the sower sowing seeds, what did the seed represent?
   a. Faith
   b. The word of God

c. Love

d. Mustard

6. What was about to happen? "It would take a small fortune to buy food for all this crowd" (Mark 6:37).

a. The arrest of Jesus

b. The Sermon on the Mount

c. The feeding of the five thousand

d. Bartholomew's winning the lottery

7. After Jesus fed the five thousand, how much food was left over?

a. None

b. Twelve basketfuls

c. A few small fish, which were set free in the Sea of Galilee

d. Three tacos and a large order of fries

8. According to Jesus, what makes someone unclean (Mark 7:20-22, NIV)?

a. Not washing hands properly

b. Stealing a neighbor's property

c. The evils from inside one's heart

d. Blood, sweat, and tears

9. At the Transfiguration, what did the voice from the cloud say (Mark 9:7)?

a. "What I have written, I have written."

b. "This is my beloved Son. Listen to him."

c. "Honor these faithful ones on the mountain of my delight."

d. "Moses led, Elijah challenged, but Jesus will save."

10. What did Jesus say the money changers and merchants had turned the temple, a house of prayer, into?

a. A bank

b. A den of robbers

c. A haven for Gentiles

d. A profitable house of prayer

11. **The teachers of the law knew that the Messiah would be whose son?**
    a. David's
    b. Mary's
    c. Caesar's
    d. Joseph's

12. **What was Jesus talking about when he said, "Not one stone will be left on top of another" (Mark 13:2)?**
    a. The wall of Nineveh
    b. The magnificent buildings of the temple
    c. The pyramids of Egypt, because they enslaved God's people
    d. His own tomb

13. **How much money did Jesus see a poor widow put in the temple treasury?**
    a. Two small copper coins
    b. Her entire fortune, ten talents of gold
    c. Twenty pieces of silver
    d. None, but she took out $2.73.

14. **According to Jesus, why was the widow's gift greater than all the others?**
    a. She gave with a pure heart.
    b. It was all she had.
    c. The others just pretended to give.
    d. Those coins were collector's items.

15. **When Jesus got to Bethany, this person had already been dead four days.**
    a. Lazarus
    b. John the Baptist
    c. Jairus's daughter
    d. The centurion

16. **What did the devil offer if Jesus worshiped him?**
    a. Wealth and pleasure
    b. All the kingdoms of the world
    c. An end to all temptation
    d. Lakers tickets

17. **Jesus was asked, "Why do you eat and drink with tax collectors and 'sinners'?" (Luke 5:30, NIV). What was his answer?**
    a. "All are God's children."
    b. "Judge not, lest you be judged."
    c. "It is not the healthy who need a doctor, but the sick."
    d. "They make better grub."

18. **Jesus went to his hometown synagogue and read a passage from Isaiah about the "Suffering Servant." Then what did he do?**
    a. Walked out
    b. Sat down and said, "This Scripture has come true today before your very eyes!"
    c. Selected four disciples from the congregation
    d. Explained to the people how he would suffer for their sins

19. **What happened when Jesus saw a funeral procession coming out of the town of Nain (Luke 7:12)?**
    a. Jesus tried to cheer up the mourners.
    b. Jesus raised the dead person—a widow's only son—back to life.
    c. Pharisees criticized them for holding a procession on the Sabbath.
    d. They collided with Jesus' disciples.

20. **What did Jesus ask his disciples when they were afraid of being drowned in the storm?**
    a. "Where is your faith?"
    b. "Didn't you see how I raised Lazarus?"
    c. "Why is your physical life so important to you?"
    d. "Why isn't anyone rowing?"

CRAZY ADS

Product

Loaves and Fishes Instant Dinners

When you have to feed a crowd on short notice. Available in 5,000- or 4,000-count packs. Great as leftovers too!

QUIZ 2D—4

1. **Luke mentions Mary Magdalene; Joanna, the wife of Herod's business manager; and Susanna. Who were these women?**
   a. Wives of some of the disciples
   b. Followers who traveled with Jesus and supported him
   c. Prostitutes sent by enemies to tempt Jesus and his disciples
   d. The real authors of Matthew, Mark, and Luke

2. **What did James and John want to do to the village that did not welcome them on their way to Jerusalem?**
   a. Call the whole town out to meet Jesus
   b. Call down fire from heaven to destroy it
   c. March around the town, praying for its citizens
   d. Play loud music in the middle of the night

3. **Who said it? "Lord, doesn't it seem unfair to you that my sister just sits here while I do all the work? Tell her to come and help me" (Luke 10:40).**
   a. Mary Magdalene
   b. Lazarus
   c. Martha
   d. Esther

4. **According to Jesus, what happens when you "keep on knocking"?**
   a. The door will be opened.
   b. Your neighbors will be annoyed.
   c. You will gain a hundredfold in heaven.
   d. Your engine needs a tune-up.

5. **According to Jesus, what people were "filthy—full of greed and wickedness," despite their sparkling exteriors?**
   a. Pharisees
   b. Pilate and Herod
   c. Tax collectors
   d. Miss America contestants

6. **You are worth more than many of these birds.**
   a. Sparrows
   b. Penguins
   c. Eagles
   d. Beagles

7. **On what day did Jesus heal a woman who had been bent double for eighteen years and couldn't stand up straight?**
   a. Passover
   b. The Sabbath
   c. The last day of his public ministry
   d. Her birthday

8. **What city did Jesus weep over, saying he wanted to gather her children together as a hen protects her chicks?**
   a. Rome
   b. Jerusalem
   c. Bethlehem
   d. Chicago

9. **What did the poor man named Lazarus do every day?**
   a. Counted his money
   b. Prayed through the Psalms
   c. Begged at the rich man's gate
   d. All of the above

10. **Who kept poor Lazarus company?**
   a. His wife and kids
   b. Job's friends

c. The dogs

d. The rich man

11. Where did Lazarus go after he died?

a. Abraham's side

b. A place of fiery torment

c. To the cemetery

d. To heaven in a chariot of fire

12. Who wanted Abraham to get a message to his five brothers, so they could avoid his fate?

a. Lazarus

b. The rich man who had ignored Lazarus

c. Simon Peter

d. All of the above

13. Who told Zacchaeus, "I must be a guest in your home today"?

a. Simon Peter

b. Caiaphas

c. Jesus

d. Mrs. Zacchaeus

14. What did Zacchaeus do for a living?

a. He was a fisherman.

b. He had a government job in Jericho.

c. He was a tax collector.

d. He modeled.

15. This person who talked with Jesus had been married five times. Who was it?

a. Nicodemus

b. The Samaritan woman at the well

c. Thomas

d. Pontius Pilate

16. **Who was the man who was "not the light; he came only as a witness to the light" (John 1:8, NIV)?**
    a. John the Baptist
    b. Peter
    c. Isaiah
    d. Jesus

17. **When the priests asked John the Baptist who he was, what did he say?**
    a. Just a baptizer
    b. I'm no one of note.
    c. I am a voice shouting in the wilderness, "Prepare a straight pathway for the Lord's coming!"
    d. Your worst nightmare

18. **In John's Gospel, what did John the Baptist say when he first saw Jesus?**
    a. "Look! There is the Lamb of God."
    b. "Let me stoop to untie your sandals."
    c. "All of my followers, follow him."
    d. "Howdy, Cousin."

19. **What time of day did Nicodemus come to talk to Jesus?**
    a. High noon
    b. At night
    c. Dawn
    d. Right after *Oprah*

20. **Finish this verse: "For God so loved the world that he gave his only Son . . ." (John 3:16)**
    a. that is, Jesus, the lamb of his love.
    b. and the Son loved the world so much he gave his life.
    c. to demolish the law and offer pardon to all.
    d. so that everyone who believes in him will not perish but have eternal life.

CRAZY ADS

Business
Zacchaeus Collection Agency
Never come up short again

Dumb Jokes

Q: What was Jesus' favorite kind of fish?
A: Fillet of soul

Q: What kind of attitudes did Jesus want his followers to have?
A: Beatitudes

Q: When Jesus dined with Zacchaeus, who made the meal?
A: A short-order cook

Q: What did Zacchaeus use on his bulletin board?
A: Tax

QUIZ 2D—5

1. What favor did Jesus ask of the Samaritan woman?
   a. He asked her for a drink of water.
   b. He wanted directions to Jacob's well.
   c. He wanted her to introduce him to the town leaders.
   d. He wanted to know where he could buy some Samaritan strudel.

2. Why was the woman so surprised at Jesus' question?
   a. She was covered with dust from the road.
   b. He was surrounded by his disciples at the time.
   c. He was Jewish, and Jews did not normally associate with Samaritans.
   d. All of the above

3. **Who said it? "He told me everything I ever did!"**
   (John 4:39).
   a. Nathanael to Philip
   b. The Samaritan woman to her townspeople
   c. Jesus, about Simon Peter
   d. King Herod, about John the Baptist

4. **Why would sick people gather around the pool of**
   Bethesda?
   a. A clinic opened there twice a month.
   b. They hoped that Jesus would come there.
   c. Roman officials collected taxes there.
   d. Every so often an angel stirred up the water, giving it
      healing power.

5. **What did the people intend to do to Jesus after he fed the**
   five thousand?
   a. Make him king
   b. Listen to his teaching
   c. Follow him to Jerusalem
   d. Ask him for dessert

6. **Who mockingly urged Jesus to go to Jerusalem to show**
   himself to the world?
   a. His mother
   b. His brothers
   c. His disciples
   d. John the Baptist

7. **A woman caught in the act of adultery was brought to**
   Jesus for judgment. What did he do?
   a. He began to write on the ground with his finger.
   b. He quoted the Old Testament laws on adultery.
   c. He named the sins of her accusers.
   d. He turned away from her.

8. **Who said it? "All right, stone her. But let those who have never sinned throw the first stones!" (John 8:7).**
   a. Caiaphas
   b. The centurion who arrested the Samaritan woman
   c. Jesus
   d. Moses

9. **Whom did Jesus tell to "Go and sin no more" (John 8:11)?**
   a. Zacchaeus
   b. A woman captured in the act of adultery
   c. Barabbas
   d. The thief beside him on the cross

10. **Fill in the blank: Jesus made a strong statement about his divinity when he said, "Before _____ was, I am" (John 8:58, KJV).**
    a. God
    b. Abraham
    c. Mary
    d. anything

11. **According to Jesus, who "was a murderer from the beginning and has always hated the truth" (John 8:44)?**
    a. Barabbas
    b. Herod
    c. The devil
    d. Cain

12. **How did Jesus heal the man born blind?**
    a. He told him to imagine that he saw trees walking.
    b. He put mud on the man's eyes and told him to wash in the pool of Siloam.
    c. He placed his hand over the man's face and prayed loudly.
    d. He used laser surgery.

13. **Why did Martha not want the stone removed from Lazarus's tomb?**
    a. There would be a bad odor.
    b. She didn't want any false hope.
    c. Her pet animals might rush inside.
    d. The mourners would criticize the appearance of the tomb.

14. **How did Jesus indicate at the Passover meal which disciple was going to betray him?**
    a. He told the two disciples sitting closest to him.
    b. He dipped a piece of bread in the dish and gave it to that disciple.
    c. He turned his back on that man during the meal.
    d. He pointed.

15. **Which of the following was *not* one of the twelve disciples of Jesus?**
    a. Bartholomew
    b. Zacchaeus
    c. James the son of Alphaeus
    d. Simon the Zealot

16. **Which of the following groups includes three of Jesus' twelve apostles?**
    a. Andrew, Thomas, Judas
    b. John, Zechariah, Malachi
    c. Simeon, Joseph, Benjamin
    d. Nathanael, Timothy, Mark

17. **How many men with leprosy did Jesus heal on his way to Jerusalem (Luke 17:11-19)?**
    a. None, because no one asked
    b. Two
    c. Ten
    d. More than the sands of the seashore

18. **How many of the former lepers returned to thank Jesus?**
    a. None
    b. One
    c. Five
    d. All of them

19. **Finish this verse: "The spirit is willing, but the body is _____" (Matt. 26:41, NIV).**
    a. rebellious
    b. flesh
    c. weak
    d. unwilling

20. **What did the three waiting disciples do while Jesus was praying in Gethsemane?**
    a. They prayed for him.
    b. They fell asleep.
    c. They alerted the temple guard.
    d. They hid.

CRAZY ADS

Product
Major League Disciple Trading Cards
    All the stats you want—all the action you need!
    Collect 'em and trade 'em with your friends!
    Now with a stick of fish-flavored bubble gum

Product
Naïve Bottled Water
    Straight from Jacob's Well in Samaria
    Serve this water and people will know more about you than you do.

Dumb Jokes

Q: How did the Samaritan woman realize Jesus was no ordinary man?
A: He knew her too "well."

Q: Why couldn't Peter walk on water?

A: His faith "wave"ered.

QUIZ 2D—6: PASSION WEEK

1. **As he prayed in Gethsemane, what did Jesus ask the Father to take from him, if possible?**
    a. This cup of suffering
    b. This bread of discontent
    c. The cross of shame
    d. His fear of dying

2. **Who crossed the Kidron Valley to enter an olive grove where he was arrested?**
    a. Absalom
    b. Jeremiah
    c. Jesus
    d. Al Capone

3. **What did Malchus lose (for a while) in Gethsemane?**
    a. His wits
    b. His faith
    c. His arm
    d. His ear

4. **Who said it? "Woman, I don't even know the man!" (Luke 22:57).**
    a. Nathanael, about Jesus
    b. Peter, about Jesus
    c. Pilate to his wife
    d. Martha to Mary

5. **Who accompanied Joseph of Arimathea when he went to Pilate to ask for Jesus' body?**
    a. Peter
    b. John

c. Nicodemus

d. Judas

6. **To whom was it said? "You believe because you have seen me. Blessed are those who haven't seen me and believe anyway" (John 20:29).**
   a. The woman caught in adultery
   b. The Samaritan woman
   c. Thomas
   d. Pilate

7. **Pilate said, "What I have written, I have written" (John 19:22). What had he written?**
   a. A letter of resignation
   b. The sign on Jesus' cross, calling him King of the Jews
   c. The death sentence for Jesus
   d. His memoirs, naming names

8. **At Jesus' crucifixion, what did soldiers throw dice for?**
   a. His seamless robe
   b. The right to pierce Jesus' side
   c. The crown of thorns
   d. Money

9. **After the crucifixion, several disciples were fishing all night. At dawn, whom did they see on shore, presumably cooking breakfast?**
   a. Martha
   b. Roman soldiers
   c. Jesus
   d. Bob Evans

10. **Who said it? "Am I some dangerous criminal . . . that you have come armed with swords and clubs to arrest me?" (Luke 22:52).**
    a. Barabbas
    b. Simon Peter

c. Malchus

d. Jesus

11. On the day of Jesus' crucifixion, what strange event happened between noon and 3 P.M.?

a. No one was able to pray.

b. Rivers and streams stopped flowing.

c. Darkness fell across the whole land.

d. All curtains were torn in two.

12. Who said it? "Surely this was a righteous man" (Luke 23:47, NIV).

a. The rabbi who sealed Jesus' tomb

b. Nicodemus

c. A Roman centurion at Jesus' crucifixion

d. Jesus, about Lazarus

13. Who said it? "Didn't our hearts feel strangely warm as he talked with us on the road and explained the Scriptures to us?" (Luke 24:32).

a. Peter, James, and John

b. Martha and Mary

c. The Ethiopian official

d. The disciples Jesus met on the road to Emmaus

14. Who said it? "Do not be so surprised. You are looking for Jesus, the Nazarene, who was crucified. He isn't here!" (Mark 16:6).

a. Peter

b. An angel

c. Pilate

d. The disciples on the road to Emmaus

15. About whom was Jesus talking? "Far better for him if he had never been born!" (Mark 14:21).

a. Caiaphas, the priest

b. Judas, his betrayer

    c. John the Baptist

    d. Moses

16. **What was Peter's reaction when he realized that he had betrayed Jesus three times as predicted?**

    a. He ran to the desert of Sinai.

    b. He killed himself.

    c. He broke down and wept.

    d. He became a high priest of Israel.

17. **To whom was it said? "The Scriptures declare, 'My Temple will be called a place of prayer,' but you have turned it into a den of thieves!" (Matt. 21:13).**

    a. Jesus' disciples

    b. The Pharisees

    c. The money changers and merchants in the temple

    d. Ali Baba

18. **What was the crowd shouting at Jesus' triumphal entry into Jerusalem?**

    a. Hosanna!

    b. Hail King Jesus!

    c. Heal me, please!

    d. All of the above

19. **How much was Judas Iscariot paid to betray Jesus?**

    a. Thirty pieces of silver

    b. Ten talents

    c. Nothing

    d. Free critiques of his personal behavior

20. **What did Jesus and his disciples do after the Last Supper, before going to the Mount of Olives?**

    a. Sang a hymn

    b. Cleaned up

    c. Prayed together

    d. Put their sandals back on

CRAZY ADS

Tabloid Headlines

The National Inspirer

"He Broke Bread with Us": Emmaus Couple Sees Risen Lord

Crucified Friday; He's Now on the Road

Soldiers Reveal Empty Tomb, Say They Slept

Book

What I Have Written, **by Pontius Pilate**

Memoirs of a not-so-innocent man

Dumb Jokes

Q: Why did Peter deny Jesus?

A: His faith "petered" out.

Q: When did the women decide they would go and anoint Jesus' body for burial?

A: Tomb-morrow

TV LISTINGS

Children's Show

Mister Rabbi

In the neighborhood this week, a lost boy from Nazareth asks some hard questions.

Sitcom

The Fresh Prince of Bethany

Rich young ruler finds he can't gain eternal life so easily. The camel scene is hilarious!

Special

Night Court

No comedy here—a secret session of the Sanhedrin railroads an innocent preacher.

2E
church chat

(ACTS—REVELATION)

QUIZ 2E—1

1. Luke wrote his Gospel to a man named Theophilus.
   To whom did he write the book of Acts?
   a. Theophilus
   b. Paul
   c. Barnabas
   d. His wife, Lulu

2. Peter gave a speech at 9 A.M. What day was it?
   a. The Sabbath
   b. One year from the day Jesus died
   c. Pentecost
   d. Ground Hog Day

3. A disciple named Joseph was given a nickname that
   means "Son of Encouragement" (Acts 4:36). What do we
   know him as?
   a. Barnabas
   b. Peter
   c. Arimathea
   d. Joseph

4. The apostles chose seven "deacons" to help them. Why?
   a. So they could spend more time in prayer and preaching
   b. They were getting older and were losing touch with
      younger Christians.
   c. No one was listening to the apostles anymore.
   d. All the business books said they needed middle
      management.

5. Who said this as he died: "Lord Jesus, receive my
   spirit. . . . Don't charge them with this sin"
   (Acts 7:59-60)?
   a. James
   b. Paul
   c. Stephen
   d. John

6. **What future missionary was watching the coats of the people who stoned Stephen?**
   a. Timothy
   b. Paul (Saul)
   c. Matthew
   d. Burlington

7. **In the desert Philip met a foreign official who was reading Old Testament prophecies about the Messiah being led like a sheep to the slaughter. What book was the man reading?**
   a. Genesis
   b. Isaiah
   c. Obadiah
   d. Acts

8. **Saul (later known as Paul) was converted on the road to Damascus. Why was he going there?**
   a. To arrest some Christians
   b. To escape from Jewish authorities
   c. To interview for a post in the Roman government
   d. To see a soccer game

9. **Why were widows weeping and showing Peter the coats Dorcas had made for them?**
   a. They were donating the garments to the poor in Jerusalem.
   b. Dorcas had died, and they wanted Peter to help her if he could.
   c. They wanted to start a charitable society in her name.
   d. They were trying to get the best price from him, but he was bidding low.

10. **Peter had a vision involving a sheet filled with nonkosher food. What was the point?**
    a. Fight temptation and keep the commandments.
    b. Rich rewards await you if you do God's will.
    c. If God says something is OK, don't say it isn't.
    d. Try to be neater next time you eat.

11. **As Saul was traveling to Damascus to persecute Christians, what knocked him to the ground?**
    a. A Roman soldier
    b. A bright light from heaven
    c. Guilt
    d. A task force of Christians

12. **About whom was this said? "But Lord . . . I've heard about the terrible things this man has done to the believers in Jerusalem! And we hear that he is authorized by the leading priests to arrest every believer in Damascus" (Acts 9:13-14).**
    a. Simon Peter
    b. Saul (Paul)
    c. Caiaphas, also known as Annas
    d. The Terminator

13. **Fill in the blank: "Claiming to be wise, they became utter _____ instead" (Rom. 1:22).**
    a. fools
    b. beasts
    c. enemies
    d. owls

14. **Romans 5:8 says God showed his great love for us by sending Christ to die for us—when?**
    a. In the fullness of time
    b. When his enemies had reached the extent of their evil
    c. While we were still sinners
    d. On Good Friday

15. **According to Romans 5, whose sin brought death to the human race?**
    a. Adam's
    b. Abraham's
    c. David's
    d. Paul's

16. In Romans 7, Paul expressed his struggle. What was it?
a. He grieved for the unbelieving Gentiles.
b. He wanted to do right, but kept doing wrong.
c. He wasn't accepted by people he preached to.
d. He really wanted to direct movies.

17. What can separate us from Christ's love (Rom. 8:38–39)?
a. Death
b. Demons
c. Worries
d. Nothing in all creation

18. What should be "living sacrifices" (Rom. 12:1)?
a. The Gentiles
b. Our children
c. Our bodies
d. Codependents

19. Finish this verse: "Do not conform any longer to the pattern of this world, but be . . ." (Rom. 12:2, NIV)
a. an enemy of the enemies of God.
b. your own person.
c. transformed by the renewing of your mind.
d. afraid to put striped patterns next to plaid patterns.

20. Who has God chosen to shame those who are powerful (1 Cor. 1:27)?
a. The powerless
b. The righteous
c. The Gentiles
d. The children

CRAZY ADS

Business
Stone Cold Dry Cleaners
We'll take your coat and have it professionally cleaned—while you're busy doing "boulder" things. Ask for Saul of Tarsus.

Services

Whiteways Sheet and Tablecloth Laundry

Don't call it unclean if we've cleansed it!

Product

Dorcas Designs

Coats and garments to meet your needs

She works herself to death for you—and then some!

QUIZ 2E—2

1. **What apostle went to the town of Joppa and raised a woman named Dorcas from the dead?**
   a. James
   b. Luke
   c. Peter
   d. Ananias

2. **Agabus, a prophet in the early church, predicted something that prompted the church in Antioch to start a relief fund for Christians in Judea (Acts 11:27-30). What did he predict?**
   a. A famine would strike.
   b. Roman authorities would soon crack down on Christians.
   c. Jerusalem would fall to Roman armies in A.D. 80.
   d. A computer glitch would throw the world into chaos.

3. **What king stepped up persecution against Christians by killing James, the brother of John?**
   a. Herod Agrippa
   b. Nero
   c. Pontius Pilate
   d. Festus

4. **What did Rhoda do after seeing who was at the door?**
   a. She left Peter standing there as she ran back inside to tell the others.

   b. She was arrested because she refused to say where the
     others were hiding.
   c. She sang a psalm of praise.
   d. She fainted.

5. **In most of the cities Paul and Barnabas visited, where did they starting preaching?**
   a. By the riverbank
   b. In the synagogue
   c. In the town hall
   d. In the pool hall

6. **Who went with Paul on his second missionary journey?**
   a. Peter
   b. Mark
   c. Silas
   d. Lydia

7. **Who had a vision of a man from Macedonia calling for help?**
   a. Barnabas
   b. Cornelius the centurion
   c. Paul
   d. John

8. **What event broke the chains of Paul and Silas in a Philippian jail?**
   a. An earthquake shook the place.
   b. An angel of the Lord appeared
   c. A bolt of lightning struck the prison house.
   d. Serge the Sledgehammer arrived.

9. **What did the Berean believers "search" to check out the teachings of Paul and Silas?**
   a. Their hearts
   b. The Scriptures
   c. Records from the other towns in Asia Minor
   d. Their pockets

10. **Paul later wrote two letters to this city, but while he was there, some people started a riot, saying, "Paul and Silas have turned the rest of the world upside down, and now they are here disturbing our city" (Acts 17:6). What city?**
    a. Ephesus
    b. Athens
    c. Thessalonica
    d. Seattle

11. **In what city did Paul see a shrine "To an Unknown God"?**
    a. Ephesus
    b. Athens
    c. Thessalonica
    d. Las Vegas

12. **Paul planted the seed in Corinth, he says, and Apollos watered it. Who made it grow?**
    a. Peter
    b. Timothy
    c. The whole church
    d. God

13. **What was Paul's advice to the unmarried and the widows?**
    a. Get married as soon as possible because the Lord is coming.
    b. Be careful to find a mate who is devout and faithful.
    c. Stay unmarried to better do the work of the Lord.
    d. Watch out for those dating services.

14. **According to 1 Corinthians 15:55, what is "swallowed up in victory"?**
    a. Pain
    b. Death
    c. Defeat
    d. Gum

15. **Finish this verse: "Wherever the Spirit of the Lord is, he gives . . ." (2 Cor. 3:17)**
    a. freedom.
    b. fighting.
    c. faith.
    d. food.

16. **Who should believers not be "yoked together" with?**
    a. Demons
    b. Weaker brothers
    c. Unbelievers
    d. Oxen

17. **Finish this verse: "I have been crucified with Christ. I myself no longer live, but . . ." (Gal. 2:19-20)**
    a. Christ lives in me.
    b. I pretend to live in order to win others.
    c. I die daily to my own desires and pleasures.
    d. my legacy lives on.

18. **Which of the following distinctions did Paul say are "no longer," for those who are one in Christ Jesus" (Gal. 3:28)?**
    a. Jew/Gentile
    b. Male/female
    c. Slave/free
    d. All of the above

19. **Finish this verse: "God forbid that I should boast about anything except . . ." (Gal. 6:14)**
    a. all that God has given me.
    b. the cross of our Lord Jesus Christ.
    c. my ministry to the lost.
    d. my amazing humility.

20. **What has Christ broken down between Jews and Gentiles (Eph. 2:14)?**
    a. The cross of shame
    b. The tower of human arrogance

c. The wall of hostility

d. The netting of mistrust

YOU SAW IT HERE FIRST

Disaster Relief

In the midst of a famine, the early church in Antioch agreed to send money to help Christians in Judea (Acts 11:27-30).

BRAIN STUFF

Remember the theme of Galatians with the simple phrase "Get A Life!" (GAL). That's sort of what Paul was saying in this letter. Some people were apparently telling the Galatians that they needed to follow the Law in order to be saved. But Paul insisted that the only way to "get a life" was by trusting in Jesus, not by following those old regulations. And if we "keep in step with the spirit" (Gal. 5:25, NIV), we'll get a life that's full of "love, joy, peace, patience, gentleness, goodness, faith, kindness, and self-control (Gal. 5:22-23, NIV).

Remember the theme of Ephesians with the simple phrase "Everyone Praise Him" (EPH). Paul makes it clear that Jews and Gentiles can join together in praising the Lord. Whether we've lived good lives or bad lives in the past, all can praise him because we're saved by God's grace, not by our own works. The whole church works together to sing God's praises and to live in ways that bring him pleasure.

Remember the theme of Philippians with the simple phrase "Perfectly Happy In Life" (PHIL). Sure, *happy* is too weak a word for the joy of following Jesus, but it works. Though Paul was in prison, he wrote about nonstop joy, whatever life may dish out. One key to this happiness is the humility of Jesus, who became a servant for our sakes. If we adopt that attitude, we'll avoid petty disputes and learn to be content with what God gives us.

Remember the theme of Colossians with the simple phrase "Christ Our Life" (COL). When others start selling you the answer to the "mystery that has been kept hidden for ages," don't buy it. In this letter Paul tells us the secret: "Christ in you, the hope of glory" (1:27, NIV). Keep Christ at the center of your life and don't fall for those hollow philosophies.

CRAZY ADS

Product
Ray-Plan Sunglasses
That sky can get awfully bright on the road to Damascus. Protect your "vision" with Ray-Plan.

Web Site
www.mission.net
Keep in touch with the latest missionary journeys. Click on now to get the new address for Barnabas and Mark.

Dumb Jokes

Q: What were Aquila and Priscilla feeling when Paul started working with them?
A: Tents

TV LISTINGS

Drama
Party of Seven
The church appoints deacons to take care of practical matters, but they share the gospel, too. This week: The widows' dispute.

Game Show
Meal of Fortune
Watch as Peter gets served questionable foods. Will he eat or not? A lot is riding on his choice. This week's guest contestant: Cornelius, the centurion.

Drama
Barney the Empire Slayer
Normally his partner gets all the press, but Barnabas was a pretty good missionary, too, taking the Good News throughout the Roman Empire.

QUIZ 2E–3

1. **About whom was it said? "This babbler has picked up some strange ideas" (Acts 17:18).**
   a. Socrates
   b. Thomas
   c. Paul
   d. The Ethiopian eunuch

2. **What couple made tents along with Paul?**
   a. Silas and Timothy
   b. Aquila and Priscilla
   c. Mary and Mark
   d. Hill and Dale

3. **Whose preaching put Eutychus to sleep?**
   a. The magistrate of Ephesus
   b. Apollos
   c. Paul
   d. Timothy

4. **Paul's nephew heard of an evil plot and told Paul about it. What were the people plotting?**
   a. To ambush and kill Paul
   b. To overthrow the Romans
   c. To persecute Christians
   d. To fill the Dead Sea with salt

5. **Paul had to stand trial before two Roman governors and a king. Who were they?**
   a. Pilate, Pliny, and Herod
   b. Felix, Festus, and Agrippa
   c. Titus, Trajan, and Antipas
   d. Thomas, Richard, and Harold

6. **To whom was it said? "You have appealed to Caesar, and to Caesar you shall go!" (Acts 25:12).**
   a. Governor Felix
   b. The Council of Philosophers in Athens
   c. Paul
   d. Agrippa

7. **After hearing Paul's story, this man asked, "Do you think you can make me a Christian so quickly?" (Acts 26:28).**
   a. Elymas the sorcerer
   b. The Philippian jailer
   c. King Agrippa
   d. Emperor Nero

8. **What difficulty did Paul face on the way to Rome?**
   a. Shipwreck
   b. Snakebite
   c. Storms
   d. All of the above

9. **The Christians of what city came out to meet Paul at the Forum on the Appian Way?**
   a. Athens
   b. Berea
   c. Caesarea
   d. Rome

10. **Who lived in a rented house in Rome, welcoming visitors and proclaiming "the Kingdom of God with all boldness" (Acts 28:31)?**
    a. The Philippian jailer
    b. Aquila and Priscilla
    c. Paul
    d. Ben-Hur

11. **According to Ephesians 5:18, what are we supposed to do instead of getting drunk?**
    a. Go to church.
    b. Meet with Christian friends for mutual encouragement.
    c. Let the Holy Spirit fill and control us.
    d. Drink root beer.

12. **Philippians 4:8 tells us to fix our thoughts on certain things. Which of the following is *not* mentioned there?**
    a. Things that are true
    b. Things that are exciting
    c. Things that are lovely
    d. Things that are right

13. **Finish this verse: "I can do everything . . ." (Phil. 4:13, NIV)**
    a. through him who gives me strength.
    b. because I believe in myself.
    c. with the support of faithful friends.
    d. once I have my morning coffee.

14. **What does the book of Colossians tell us to sing?**
    a. Psalms
    b. Hymns
    c. Spiritual songs
    d. All of the above

15. **Who was Onesimus?**
    a. The leader of the church at Corinth
    b. A runaway slave Paul was sending back to Philemon
    c. An associate of Barnabas on his journey to Cyprus
    d. The winner of the A.D. 48 Olympic decathlon

16. **Who said it? "I will never fail you. I will never forsake you" (Heb. 13:5).**
    a. Our spouses
    b. Our church leaders
    c. God
    d. Paul

17. **Finish this verse: "Do not merely listen to the word, and so deceive yourselves. . . ." (James 1:22, NIV)**
    a. Preach it to others.
    b. Do what it says.
    c. Honor it with all your heart.
    d. Underline it.

18. **According to 1 John 1:9, what happens when we confess our sin?**
    a. We earn favor with the one who is holy.
    b. God is faithful and just to forgive and cleanse us.
    c. We lose the respect of unbelievers.
    d. If we sign a book contract, we can make oodles of money.

19. **First John is a book about love, but what does it tell us not to love (1 John 2:15)?**
    a. Ourselves
    b. This evil world and all it offers
    c. Money
    d. Mayonnaise

20. **Fill in the blank: "Look! Here I stand at the door and _____" (Rev. 3:20).**
    a. wait
    b. knock
    c. offer my great salvation
    d. sell subscriptions

CRAZY ADS

Product
Alert-X
The pill that keeps you awake, no matter how long the apostle preaches—because you don't want to miss a word!

Product
Malta Snakebite Kit
Don't get shipwrecked without it!

Dumb Jokes

Q: Who carried the coffin of the "greatest apostle" at his funeral?
A: Paul bearers

Q: Do you know what happened to the blind carpenter who was traveling on the road to Damascus?
A: He picked up a hammer and Saul.

Q: What happens when people don't keep listening to God's Word?
A: Hear today, gone tomorrow.

HIDDEN PAUL

Fifteen names or words associated with the apostle Paul are hidden in the following silly story. Can you find them? (Note: Words and names are strung between the words of the story.)

Out west, we visited the Hoover Dam, as custom would dictate. We were breaking no formal taboo, following the path, ensuring our safety, but the guard ordered us to disperse. "Cute!" I complained loudly to our leader (because I often let terse comments fly). As I lashed out, the guard tried to keep from answering at first; then he pointed. "See him? One more step, he never comes back."

Then I moved as quietly as a lamb, as sad—or as worried—as I could be. Really, straight as a post, legs stiff as an icon, I (umbrella under my arm) was red as a barn, a basket case.

Here's what you're looking for:

Ambassador	Letters
Apostle	Lystra
Athens	Malta
Barnabas	Persecute
Berea	Romans
Damascus	Silas
Derbe	Stephen
Iconium	

TV LISTINGS

Talk Show
Persistently Incorrect
Starring the apostle Paul. He tries to do right, but keeps doing wrong!

Sitcom
Saved by the Quell
An earthquake suddenly breaks the chains of Paul and Barnabas. But do they get out of jail free? No way! They want to show the jailer *true* freedom.

Drama
The Equalizer
No slave or free person, Jew or Gentile, male or female—Christ Jesus makes sure all are of equal value.

Sitcom
Rome Improvement
Paul's under house arrest, but you wouldn't know it! Even in the heart of the Roman Empire, people keep coming to him and he keeps talking about Jesus.

Game Show
Jeopardy!
Paul's nephew warns about an ambush. Will Paul give the right answers to the Roman guard and escape it?

2F
mix it up

(GENERAL INFORMATION)

QUIZ 2F—1

1. **Who said it to whom? "You intended to harm me, but God intended it for good to accomplish what is now being done, the saving of many lives" (Gen. 50:20, NIV).**
   a. David to his rebellious son Absalom
   b. Joseph to the brothers who sold him as a slave
   c. Paul to the soldiers who arrested him
   d. Jonah to the whale

2. **"It was white like coriander seed, and it tasted like honey cakes" (Exod. 16:31). What?**
   a. The meat the raven brought to Elijah
   b. The bread at the Last Supper
   c. Manna from heaven
   d. The forbidden fruit

3. **Who said it? "The land we explored devours those living in it. All the people we saw there are of great size" (Num. 13:32, NIV).**
   a. Gulliver during his travels
   b. Zacchaeus in the tree
   c. Ten of the Israelite spies who explored the Promised Land
   d. David's brothers

4. **Only one woman has the age when she died mentioned in Scripture—127 years old. Who was it?**
   a. Ruth
   b. Sarah
   c. Mary
   d. Carol Channing

5. **To whom was it said? "Be strong and courageous, because you will lead these people to inherit the land I swore to their forefathers to give them. . . . Be careful to obey all the law my servant Moses gave you" (Josh. 1:6, NIV).**
   a. Abraham
   b. Moses

c. Joshua

d. The disciples

6. **The shortest chapter in the Bible is two before the longest chapter in the Bible, and the chapter in between contains the middle verse of Scripture. What three chapters are we talking about?**

a. 2 Chronicles 12–14

b. Malachi 4; Matthew 1–2

c. Psalms 117–119

d. Joshua 24; Psalm 1; Luke 5

7. **Who said it? "What have I done to you that deserves your beating me these three times?" (Num. 22:28).**

a. Noah's wife

b. Pharaoh's son

c. The apostle Paul

d. Balaam's donkey

8. **Which of the following cities was *not* visited by Paul?**

a. Carthage

b. Corinth

c. Derbe

d. Ephesus

9. **Who said it? "God has brought me laughter, and everyone who hears about this will laugh with me" (Gen. 21:6, NIV).**

a. Sarah, at the birth of her son

b. David, after he killed Goliath

c. Esther, after the hanging of Haman

d. Stephen, before his martyrdom

10. **Which of the following rivers is *not* mentioned in Scripture?**

a. Nile

b. Tigris

c. Euphrates

d. Rhine

11. **Who said it? "That Hebrew slave you brought us came to me to make sport of me. But as soon as I screamed for help, he left his cloak beside me and ran out of the house" (Gen. 39:17, NIV).**
    a. Pharaoh's daughter, about young Moses
    b. The wife of Potiphar, who bought Joseph as a slave
    c. Naaman, the Syrian who came to the prophet Elisha for healing
    d. Pontius Pilate, before condemning Jesus

12. **Which of the following biblical items have archaeologists found?**
    a. Aaron's blooming rod
    b. A seal used by Jeremiah's scribe, Baruch
    c. One of the parchments Paul asked Timothy to bring him
    d. John the Baptist's deodorant

13. **Which of the following is the Word of God *not* compared to?**
    a. A lamp
    b. A mirror
    c. A bird of prey
    d. A hammer

14. **Which of the following was *not* an associate of Paul?**
    a. Demas
    b. Bartholomew
    c. Trophimus
    d. Mark

15. **What were 27 feet tall, topped by capitals that extended another 7 ½ feet, and connected with a network of interwoven chains and decorative pomegranates?**
    a. The Tree of Life and the Tree of Knowledge in the Garden of Eden
    b. The swords used by Canaanite warriors
    c. The two front pillars in Solomon's temple
    d. Goliath's brothers

16. **What distinction belongs to Maher-shalal-hash-baz (Isa. 8:1-3)?**
    a. He was the Assyrian king who defeated the northern kingdom.
    b. This was the full name of the queen of Sheba.
    c. He was the only one to respond to Isaiah's ministry.
    d. This is the longest name in the Bible.

17. **What book of the New Testament has the most chapters?**
    a. Matthew
    b. Mark
    c. Luke
    d. Revelation

18. **Which book of the Old Testament has the fewest verses?**
    a. Genesis
    b. Obadiah
    c. Zechariah
    d. Moses' Greatest Tips for Getting Water Out of Rocks

19. **To whom was it said? "Obedience is far better than sacrifice" (1 Sam. 15:22).**
    a. Abraham, after he nearly killed Isaac
    b. King Saul, after he disobeyed God's orders
    c. Elijah, after his victory on Mount Carmel
    d. King Herod, after beheading John the Baptist

20. **Who described himself as "the king's cup-bearer"?**
    a. Joseph
    b. David
    c. Nehemiah
    d. Juan Valdez

YOU SAW IT HERE FIRST

Dysfunctional Families
Nowadays that's all you hear about—divorce, abandonment, denial, scheming, and so on. Many families just don't work as they should.

Well, Freud didn't invent all that. Scripture has several contenders for the title of First Dysfunctional Family. Life in David's family was no picnic. He was a good man, but probably not a good father. One son attacked his half sister and was murdered by his half brother, Absalom, who later rebelled against David. We're not talking teenage rebellion here. This was a national revolution.

But long before David, the patriarchal family of Isaac and Rebekah takes the cake. We see trickery between this husband and wife, and Uncle Laban and Jacob were always deceiving each other. There's massive sibling rivalry between Jacob and Esau, then between Rachel and Leah, and later among Jacob's sons. A modern shrink would have had a field day!

But if God could do such great things among such messed up families, maybe you're future isn't so bleak after all.

Dumb Jokes

Q: How do we know there was tennis in the Bible?
A: Joseph served in Pharaoh's court.

Q: How do we know there was tennis in the Bible?
A: James and John were mending their net.

HIDDEN OT PLACES

The names of nine OT places are hidden in the following nonsense story. Can you find them? (Note: Words are strung between the words of the story.)

"Can A and B both be right?" the drama student wondered. "I might have to redo my exam." This beauty really turned heads as she entered the restaurant, smelling of lilac. "Hi," she said to the casting director who bought her a drink. (You can bet he longed to know her better.) "I do thank you. Nevertheless I don't drink beer," she baldly asserted. "Fine," he countered, "but I have nine vehicles for some actress. *Sound of Music* needs a Maria who can sing at her own pace. We have no stars." His humorless voice went on. "They've gone the way of the dinosaurs. The brontosaurus deserves an elegy. Pterodactyls, tyrannosaurs, all gone."

Here's what you're looking for:

Beersheba   Gath
Bethel   Lachish
Canaan   Samaria
Dothan   Tyre
Edom

QUIZ 2F—2: BY THE NUMBERS

1. One is the number of . . .

    a. sons of Isaac.

    b. years Paul had to wait before meeting the disciples.

    c. healed lepers who returned to thank Jesus.

    d. Bible books written by Maynard, the unknown disciple.

2. Two is the number of . . .

    a. spies who recommended that the Israelites invade Canaan.

    b. sons of Jacob.

    c. years of Jesus' ministry.

    d. times per day you should read the whole Bible through.

3. Three is the number of . . .

    a. sons of Abraham.

    b. days Jonah was in the belly of the fish.

    c. testaments.

    d. square meals Jesus had each day while fasting in the desert.

4. Four is the number of . . .

    a. people the king saw in the fiery furnace.

    b. lions in the den with Daniel.

    c. books of the Bible written by John.

    d. songs that David kept playing for Saul, over and over.

5. Five is the number of . . .

    a. Bible books credited to Moses.

    b. sons of Jesse.

    c. Beatitudes.

    d. species that Noah would not let on board the ark.

6. Six is the number of . . .
a. loaves of bread a little boy let Jesus multiply.
b. days God took to create things.
c. friends of Job.
d. disciples who told Peter he was crazy for trying to walk on water.

7. Seven is the number of . . .
a. times Naaman was told to dip in the Jordan River.
b. daughters of Laban.
c. Bible books written by Paul.
d. pieces of silver the magi paid for that frankincense.

8. Eight is the number of . . .
a. people on the ark.
b. commandments God really gave on Mount Sinai.
c. fish caught by Peter after he denied Jesus.
d. bears Elisha called out of the woods to terrorize some ornery kids.

9. Nine is the number of . . .
a. stones David slung before hitting Goliath.
b. soldiers who tried on Saul's armor before David did.
c. feet tall, approximately, that Goliath was.
d. times Goliath laughed at David before getting beaned.

10. Ten is the number of . . .
a. brothers of Goliath who swore vengeance against David.
b. husbands of Ruth before she fell in love with Boaz.
c. virgins in Jesus' parable who took enough oil for their lamps.
d. centuries in which Methuselah lived.

11. Eleven is the number of . . .
a. brothers of Joseph.
b. disciples of Jesus.
c. chapters in Genesis.
d. laundromats in Eden.

12. Twelve is the number of . . .
a. brothers of Joseph.
b. disciples of Jesus.
c. chapters in 1 Corinthians.
d. the square root of the Beast.

13. Thirteen is the number of . . .
a. fruit flies on the ark.
b. the famous "love chapter" of 1 Corinthians.
c. the infamous "hate chapter" of Ecclesiastes.
d. years old Jesus was when the magi visited.

14. Fourteen is the number of . . .
a. total years Jacob worked so he could marry Rachel.
b. bad dreams Jacob had before reuniting with Esau.
c. rungs on the ladder Jacob saw ascending toward heaven.
d. lentils in the stew Jacob made for Esau.

15. Fifteen is the number of . . .
a. people of Nineveh who responded to Jonah's message.
b. years God added to Hezekiah's life after he prayed for healing.
c. days Elisha had to wait to get his prophet license.
d. sons of Jacob, before that tragic accident with Manny, Moe, and Jack.

16. Sixteen is the number of . . .
a. years the Israelites wandered minus days of creation.
b. gifts the magi offered times Jesus' disciples.
c. number of Gospels squared.
d. people who can pronounce the name Mephibosheth.

17. Twenty is the number of . . .
a. pieces of silver the slave traders paid for Joseph.
b. years the Israelites were in Babylonian captivity.
c. friends who advised Job.
d. bottles of wine Jesus turned to water.

18. Thirty is the number of . . .

    a. pieces of silver Judas got for betraying Jesus.

    b. spies who recommended *not* invading Canaan.

    c. days Noah was aboard the ark.

    d. people who fell asleep during Paul's preaching.

19. Forty is the number of . . .

    a. pieces of silver Delilah got for Samson's hair.

    b. years the Israelites wandered in the wilderness.

    c. people who became Christians on the day of Pentecost.

    d. wives that Solomon felt he could actually talk to.

20. Fifty is the number of . . .

    a. pieces of silver Aaron paid for the golden calf.

    b. commandments Jesus broke by picking grain on the Sabbath.

    c. books of the Bible.

    d. years that went by before the Israelites were supposed to free all the slaves.

21. Sixty is the number of . . .

    a. years old David was when he committed adultery.

    b. years old Abraham was when he fathered Isaac.

    c. the minimum age of widows Timothy was told to put on the "widows' list."

    d. the mandatory retirement age for a king of Israel.

22. Seventy is the number of . . .

    a. disciples Jesus sent out two by two.

    b. years the Israelites were held captive by the Philistines.

    c. churches in the book of Revelation.

    d. times the disciples had to wave the John 3:16 sign before Nicodemus finally got it.

23. Ninety is the number of . . .

    a. verses in the Bible's longest chapter.

    b. years old Sarah was when she bore Isaac.

    c. churches visited by Paul and Barnabas.

    d. letters in the names of most minor prophets.

24. One hundred is the number of . . .

    a. soldiers led by a centurion.

    b. days in Daniel's seventieth "week."

    c. disciples who fled when Jesus was crucified.

    d. times Adam reminded Eve that she ate the apple first.

25. Three hundred is the number of . . .

    a. kings of Israel who were unfaithful to God.

    b. soldiers Gideon used to rout an army of thousands.

    c. days the sun stood still for Joshua.

    d. times you should forgive someone before getting even.

26. One thousand is the number of . . .

    a. people who became Christians on the day of Pentecost.

    b. bricks the Israelites had to make for the Egyptians per
       hour.

    c. years that one day is like to the Lord.

    d. times Martha had to tell Mary to mind her manners.

AMAZING FACTS

The Bible wasn't divided into chapters until the 1200s. Verses didn't show up until the 1500s.

Dumb Jokes: Teams

Q: What basketball team would John the Baptist play for?

A: The Trailblazers

Q: What basketball team would fishermen James and John play for?

A: The Nets

Q: What baseball team could David try out for as he ran from Saul?

A: The Dodgers

Q: What was Peter's baseball team?

A: The Rockies

QUIZ 2F—3: FIND THE BOOK
What book would you turn to if you wanted to find . . .

1. **The Beatitudes**
   a. Psalms
   b. Matthew
   c. Philippians
   d. Revelation

2. **Angels appearing to shepherds**
   a. 2 Chronicles
   b. Isaiah
   c. Luke
   d. Revelation

3. **"I am the way, the truth, and the life."**
   a. Ecclesiastes
   b. John
   c. Romans
   d. 1 John

4. **Instructions about skin diseases**
   a. Genesis
   b. Leviticus
   c. Romans
   d. *Seventeen*

5. **Samson's shear disaster**
   a. Judges
   b. Exodus
   c. Psalms
   d. *Hair Care for Dummies*

6. **"The Lord is my light."**
   a. Joshua
   b. Psalms
   c. 1 Corinthians
   d. Westinghouse

7. A prophet told to marry an unfaithful woman
a. Judges
b. Proverbs
c. Hosea
d. *The Book of Virtues*

8. The seventh seal
a. Genesis
b. Daniel
c. Revelation
d. *Good Housekeeping*

9. The queen of Sheba
a. Numbers
b. 1 Kings
c. Acts
d. *The King and I*

10. The crossing of the Red Sea
a. Exodus
b. Joshua
c. Ezra
d. *Red Badge of Courage*

11. Jericho's wall fall
a. Genesis
b. Joshua
c. Luke
d. *Home Remodeling*

12. The wise men who visit baby Jesus
a. Isaiah
b. Acts
c. Matthew
d. Frankincense

13. "To everything there is a season."
   a. Psalms
   b. Ecclesiastes
   c. Romans
   d. *Farmer's Almanac*

14. The Good Samaritan
   a. Luke
   b. Jeremiah
   c. Acts
   d. AAA Travel Guide

15. Peter meditating on a rooftop
   a. Matthew
   b. 1 Peter
   c. Simon Says
   d. Acts

16. David's giant victory
   a. Joshua
   b. 1 Samuel
   c. Psalms
   d. The Philistine Prophecy

17. Boaz, Naomi, and Orpah
   a. Numbers
   b. Ruth
   c. Esther
   d. *The Young and the Restless*

18. A Jewish girl becomes queen of Persia
   a. Numbers
   b. Ruth
   c. Esther
   d. *Chicken Soup for the Soul*

19. The woman Jesus met at the well
   a. Matthew
   b. John
   c. Galatians
   d. *The Fountainhead*

20. "Who can find a virtuous and capable wife?"
   a. Ruth
   b. Proverbs
   c. 1 Timothy
   d. *Great Expectations*

21. Balaam's talking donkey
   a. Numbers
   b. 2 Chronicles
   c. Acts
   d. *The Horse Whisperer*

22. "May your kisses be as exciting as the best wine."
   a. Ruth
   b. Song of Songs
   c. James
   d. *Hershey's Guide to Chocolate*

AMAZING FACTS

The word for Adam's *rib* can also mean *side*.

There are no cats in the Bible.

The King James Version mentions the "unicorn" in several passages (Num. 23:22; Job 39:9-12; Ps. 29:6), but this is a misunderstanding of the Hebrew word *re'em*. It refers to a horned creature, all right, but one with two horns. Modern translations call it a wild ox.

MINI-QUIZ: FAMOUS FIRSTS

1. Who was the first child mentioned in Scripture?

2. What is the first commandment given in Scripture?

3. She wore the first bridal veil in Scripture (Gen. 24:65), though she didn't have anything to hide from her husband—until much later. Who wore it?

4. Who told the first lie in the Bible?

5. Melchizedek was the first priest in the Bible. He received a contribution from what man?

6. Nimrod was the first mentioned in Scripture to conduct a certain activity (Gen. 10:9). In fact his name became proverbial in this "sport." What was it?

QUIZ 2F—4: ANGELS

1. Angels were climbing up and down this structure in Jacob's dream (Gen. 28:12).
   a. The tabernacle or temple
   b. The ark of the covenant
   c. A staircase or ladder
   d. The Crystal Cathedral

2. An angel with a sword blocked the path of this prophet and his donkey (Num. 22:21-35).
   a. Micaiah
   b. Balaam
   c. Moses
   d. Elisha

3. An angel cared for this depressed prophet, telling him to "Get up and eat" (1 Kings 19:5-8).
   a. Samuel
   b. Elijah
   c. Haggai
   d. Jonah

4. An angel touched this prophet's lips with a burning coal.

a. Elijah

b. Isaiah

c. Jeremiah

d. Hot Lips Houlihan

5. An angel apparently kept Shadrach, Meshach, and Abednego cool in this place of punishment.

a. The king's dungeon

b. The lions' den

c. The blazing furnace

d. Study hall

6. An angel kept these creatures from eating Daniel.

a. Lions

b. Tigers

c. Bears

d. Oh, my!

7. An angel announced the birth of John the Baptist to this dumbstruck father.

a. Joseph

b. Ananias

c. Zechariah

d. MmmmMMmm-mmNNmmMmmm

8. Angels "took care of" Jesus after this desert ordeal.

a. His temptation

b. His baptism

c. His interview with the rabbis in the temple

d. His SATs

9. An angel "came down from heaven and rolled aside" this stone.

a. The cornerstone of the temple

b. The millstone that Samson was turning

c. The stone at the door of Jesus' tomb

d. The stone that struck Goliath in the forehead

10. **An angel sprang this disciple from prison, though he was chained between two guards.**
    a. Peter
    b. John
    c. Thomas
    d. Clyde

QUIZ 2F—5: SIBLINGS

1. **Brother of Haran and Nahor**
   a. Adam
   b. Abimelech
   c. Andrew
   d. Abraham

2. **Half brother of Ishmael**
   a. Hagar
   b. Isaac
   c. Jacob
   d. Kenny

3. **Leah's prettier sister**
   a. Rachel
   b. Rebekah
   c. Ruth
   d. Ricki Lake

4. **Dinah's youngest half brother**
   a. Benjamin
   b. Joseph
   c. Reuben
   d. Pauly

5. **Manasseh's brother and the head of a half-tribe**
   a. Simeon
   b. Samaria

    c. Ephraim
    d. Manny

6. Sister to Moses and Aaron
    a. Mary
    b. Miriam
    c. Martha
    d. Mimi

7. Brother of Tamar and the murderous half brother of Amnon
    a. Solomon
    b. Mephibosheth
    c. Rayon
    d. Absalom

8. He stole his brother Philip's wife, Herodias
    a. Agrippa
    b. Pilate
    c. Festus
    d. Herod

9. The brother Andrew brought to Jesus
    a. Simon Peter
    b. Simon the Zealot
    c. Stephen
    d. Sammy

10. Half brother of James, Joseph, Simon, and Judas
    a. Bartholomew
    b. Thomas of Arimathea
    c. Zacchaeus
    d. Jesus

MINI-QUIZ: NAME CHANGES
Match each person with his or her alternate name.

1. Jacob	a. Hadassah
2. Joseph	b. Zaphenath-paneah
3. Naomi	c. Joseph of Cyprus
4. Esther	d. Belteshazzar
5. Daniel	e. Israel
6. Peter	f. Mara
7. Paul	g. Simon Bar-Jonah
8. Barnabas	h. Saul

AMAZING FACTS
You could read through the entire Bible *out loud* in a year in just twelve minutes a day.

Polls have indicated that one in nine Americans (11 percent) reads the Bible daily. Another two in nine (22 percent) read it weekly. Nearly half (48 percent) read it less than once a month or never. The good news: The numbers are a little better for teenagers.

PART 3:

secret stuff

3A
start-up

(GENESIS – 1 SAMUEL)

QUIZ 3A—1

1. **The New Testament tells women, "You are her daughters when you do what is right without fear of what your husbands might do" (1 Peter 3:6). Who is it talking about?**
   a. Abraham's daughter, Canaan
   b. Abraham's wife, Sarah
   c. Abraham's servant, Hagar
   d. Abraham's therapist, Amanda

2. **God promised that Abraham would be the father of a great nation—his descendants would be as numerous as . . .**
   a. stars in the sky
   b. sand on the shore
   c. animals in the ark
   d. McDonald's franchises

3. **Why did God put a mark on Cain?**
   a. To punish him
   b. So he could tell him apart from Abel
   c. To protect him from violence
   d. To help popularize tattoos

4. **Seth, Enosh, Kenan, and Mahalel were . . .**
   a. four rivers in the Garden of Eden
   b. four types of fruit Adam and Eve were permitted to eat
   c. descendants of Adam and Eve
   d. lawyers who sued the serpent for fraud

5. **According to Genesis 5:24 (NIV), a man named Enoch "walked with God" and then apparently vanished ("was no more"). Why?**
   a. God took him away.
   b. He dishonored the name of the Lord.
   c. He was an angel.
   d. He was never all there to begin with.

6. What did Noah do when he got out of the ark?
a. Kissed the ground
b. Danced naked
c. Sang a song of praise
d. Sacrificed some of the animals

7. How did God destroy the wicked cities of Sodom and Gomorrah?
a. They sank into the Dead Sea.
b. He rained down burning sulfur on them.
c. An earthquake destroyed it.
d. High taxes

8. What was Hagar's relationship to Abraham?
a. It was the mountain where he died.
b. He was the priest Abraham honored.
c. She was a servant girl who bore Abraham's son Ishmael.
d. They never knew each other.

9. Why did Hagar run away from Abraham's household?
a. There was a drought in the land.
b. An angel told her to.
c. She wasn't getting along with Abraham's wife.
d. She dreamed of singing in the nightclubs of Egypt.

10. Abraham asked God to spare the city of Sodom if he found how many righteous people there?
a. Fifty
b. Thirty
c. Ten
d. All of the above

11. Who said that his wife was his sister so he wouldn't be killed?
a. Abraham
b. Isaac
c. Both Abraham and Isaac
d. None of the above

12. **Meditating in the fields, Isaac looked up and saw camels approaching. Who was he about to see for the first time?**
    a. His real mother, Hagar
    b. His wife, Rebekah
    c. His sons, Jacob and Esau
    d. His agent, Sid

13. **When neighboring herdsmen claimed for themselves a well that Isaac's servants had dug, what did Isaac do?**
    a. Declared war against the five kings of the Philistines
    b. Claimed their herds for himself
    c. Asked God to send burning sulfur on their city
    d. Dug another well

14. **Joseph and Benjamin were Jacob's favorite sons. Why?**
    a. They worked the hardest in the fields.
    b. They loved God more than the others.
    c. They were the only sons of Jacob's favorite wife, Rachel.
    d. They made a great doubles team at badminton.

15. **How did Jacob throw his hip out of joint?**
    a. Wrestling with a mysterious man who may have been God himself
    b. Running from an angry warrior who was probably his brother, Esau
    c. Hunting for a deer he saw near the Jabbok Brook
    d. Jumping out of bed when he found Leah there instead of Rachel

16. **Melchizedek (mel-KIZ-uh-DEK) was a priest and king who blessed Abraham after a battle. What did Abraham do in return?**
    a. Blessed him back
    b. Humbly refused to accept the blessing
    c. Gave him a tenth of the spoils from the battle
    d. Asked him how to pronounce his name

17. How did Rachel die?
   a. Killed by Esau's warriors
   b. Giving birth to Benjamin
   c. Poisoned by her sister, Leah
   d. In a tragic sheepherding accident

18. Joseph interpreted dreams of two fellow prisoners, predicting what lay ahead for each of them. Were his predictions good, bad, or mixed?
   a. Both good. They would be freed from prison.
   b. Both bad. They would both be killed.
   c. Mixed. One would die; the other would be set free.
   d. Mixed. Both would be freed and given new jobs brushing the Sphinx's teeth.

19. Pharaoh dreamed of seven fat cows and seven lean cows coming out of the river. According to Joseph, what did this mean?
   a. Seven of his royal officials were corrupt and should be replaced by common people.
   b. Seven prisoners were plotting the overthrow of Pharaoh's government.
   c. Seven years of plenty would be followed by seven years of famine.
   d. Pharaoh should go on a diet for seven years.

20. Why did Joseph hide a silver cup in his brother Benjamin's sack?
   a. He wanted to give Ben a present without the others getting jealous.
   b. He falsely accused Ben of stealing to see if the brothers would defend him.
   c. Joseph was stealing from Pharaoh's treasury.
   d. The cup was a tracking device.

AMAZING FACTS

The olive branch is a symbol for peace. That might come from Genesis 8:11, where the dove that Noah sent from the ark returned with an "olive leaf" in its beak. Practically speaking, this meant that the water had receded to the tops of the trees, but we might see the olive branch as a symbol of peace between God and humanity.

YOU SAW IT HERE FIRST

Perfume

Modern perfume makers always seek new formulas for the latest trendy scent—then they give it a spiritual-sounding name: Eternity, or something similar. Well, you can find a formula for perfume in Exodus 30:34-37. This was incense used in the tabernacle ceremonies. Just take some resin droplets, mollusk scent, and frankincense . . .

FAQ:

Q: How did the Israelites get into slavery in Egypt?

A: Ironically, it goes back to Joseph being sold as a slave and carried to Egypt. He rose to great prominence in Egypt's government, and his brothers, in a time of famine, reunited with him there in Egypt. Their descendants settled there for several centuries. "Then a new king came to the throne of Egypt who knew nothing about Joseph or what he had done" (Exod. 1:8). That's when the Egyptians enslaved the Israelites.

MAP IT OUT

You can easily map out the history of God's people in the Old Testament.

• Babylon to Canaan: Abraham's move
• Canaan to Egypt: Brothers join Joseph
• Egypt to Canaan: Red Sea and wilderness
• Canaan to Babylon: Seventy-year captivity
• Babylon to Canaan: The return(s) under Ezra, Nehemiah, etc.

CRAZY ADS

Web Site
www.babeltalk.com
The recent explosion of new languages makes our translation
services more important than ever.

Poster
Missing: Man of God
Answers to the name Enoch
Last seen: Walking with God

Service
Drinkwell Water Services
So you don't have to keep digging new wells when your neigh-
bors steal them

Product
Rejuven8
Vitamins for your tenth century of life. The latest from Methuse-
lah Labs.

Product
ShurDry Deck Sealant
For those massive downpours

Service
Mayfollow Van Lines
When you're not sure where you're going

Service
Hilarity Health Services
Private care for the expectant mother in her nineties. Because
childbirth is no laughing matter.

Service
Runaway Relocation
When you need a one-way ticket out of the city of brotherly
love—and you have to get away *fast*. Call LABOR-47; ask for
Laban.

𝒟ⓤ𝔪𝔟 𝒥ⓞ𝓴𝓮𝓼

Q: What are God's favorite creatures of the air?
A: Birds of pray

Q: What did Noah do as the animals entered the ark?
A: Noah count.

Q: What happened to Lot's wife on the way out of Sodom?
A: She was a-salt-ed.

HIDDEN JOSEPH

This nonsense paragraph hides ten words or names associated with Joseph. Can you find them? (Note: Words and names are strung between the words of the story.)

On the way home from his public relations job, Ben was caught in a pouring rain. He just wanted to dry off in his lav, ease into his favorite chair, and sip some chicken broth—er, soup. But it wasn't soup in that pot, I pharisaically noted, as I served Ben jam instead. "How was your day?" I asked. "PR is one really difficult job," he replied. "I doubt myself. Am I never going to get it right? I sent one memo titled, 'Re: a merry Christmas.' It gave me an earache." Lovingly, I tried to grab a kernel of hope.

Here's what you're looking for:

Baker	Grain
Benjamin	Potiphar
Brothers	Prisoner
Dreamer	Rachel
Famine	Slave

QUIZ 3A—2

1. How did Moses meet his wife?
   a. He rescued her and her sisters from shepherds and then drew water for their flocks.

b. He was passed out from the heat when she gave him water.

c. He rescued her from slave traders.

d. They danced together at the Sinai sock hop.

2. **Why did God ask Moses to take off his sandals?**
   a. They were made from the skin of animals, which was abominable to the Lord.
   b. He was standing on holy ground.
   c. God wanted Moses to offer his sandals as a sacrifice.
   d. They smelled really bad.

3. **When God asked Moses to go back to Egypt with a message, what did Moses say?**
   a. "They won't believe me."
   b. "I'm not a good speaker."
   c. "Who am I to appear before Pharaoh?"
   d. All of the above

4. **How did God answer Moses' excuses?**
   a. He gave Moses miracles to perform.
   b. He asked Moses who created his ability to speak.
   c. God introduced himself by name.
   d. All of the above

5. **How did the Israelites escape from the final deadly plague?**
   a. They put blood on their doorposts so the Angel of Death would "pass over" them.
   b. They hid under their tables as the Angel of Death "passed over" their homes.
   c. They journeyed three days into the desert to perform sacrifices.
   d. They crossed their fingers.

6. **When Moses raised his hand over the sea (Exod. 14:21), what happened?**
   a. His hand became afflicted with leprosy.
   b. The Lord opened up a path through the water.

c. The Egyptians stopped in their tracks.

d. The teacher called on him.

7. While all the Israelites sang their victory song, what did Miriam do?

a. Made plans for the rest of the journey to the Promised Land

b. Sat by herself in tears

c. Scolded Moses for his pride

d. Played the tambourine

8. In the desert, the Israelites camped at a place with bitter water. What did God tell Moses to do to make the bitter water better?

a. Boil it

b. Throw a branch in it

c. Pray over it

d. Add butter and flour to make pancakes, making the bitter better with butter batter.

9. When they saw the mysterious bread from heaven lying on the ground, the Israelites called it *manna*. What does *manna* mean?

a. Bread

b. Wonderful gift

c. Thanks be to God

d. What is it?

10. Why did God give the Israelites twice as much manna on the sixth day?

a. To reward them for their hard work

b. So they wouldn't have to gather food on the Sabbath

c. So they could store some for future travels

d. To feed their pets

11. **On one occasion God told Moses to strike a rock with his staff. On another, Moses was supposed to speak to the rock. What happened then?**
    a. Water gushed out.
    b. Moses got his people's attention.
    c. Lightning struck.
    d. He invented rock music.

12. **A man named Jethro gave Moses great advice: Share the leadership of Israel with a council of seventy elders. Who was Jethro?**
    a. The oldest man in Israel
    b. The son of Pharaoh
    c. Moses' father-in-law
    d. One of the Bethany Hillbillies

13. **At one point, Moses sent twelve spies into the land of Canaan. How many of them recommended that the Israelites should enter the Promised Land?**
    a. All twelve
    b. Two
    c. None
    d. Trick question. Canaan wasn't really the Promised Land.

14. **Some of the spies were impressed with the size of the Canaanites. Next to them, they said, we look like . . . ?**
    a. children.
    b. dwarves.
    c. dogs.
    d. grasshoppers.

15. **The spies reported that Canaan was "overflowing" with what two food items?**
    a. Grain and wine
    b. Fruit and olive oil
    c. Milk and honey
    d. Cheese and crackers

16. **Joshua, the next leader of Israel, was one of only two men to live through the wilderness wanderings. The other was Caleb. Why did Caleb live that long?**
    a. He ate right and exercised daily.
    b. He prayed three times a day, and so God honored him with a long life.
    c. Joshua and Caleb were the only two spies who recommended entering the Promised Land.
    d. Joshua needed Caleb as his assistant.

17. **Which of the following was *not* kept in the ark of the covenant?**
    a. Some manna
    b. Aaron's staff that budded
    c. The tablets of the Ten Commandments
    d. A gold ring from the golden calf

18. **Exodus 36:1 says that the Lord gifted Bezalel (BEZ-uh-lell), Oholiab (oh-HOLE-ee-ab), and other craftsmen with wisdom, skill, and intelligence. What was their job?**
    a. To create furnishings for the tabernacle
    b. To design the royal palace in Jerusalem
    c. To make the golden calf
    d. To write the book of Leviticus

19. **According to Old Testament Law, every fiftieth year was to be a celebration of freedom, in which slaves were freed. What was this year called?**
    a. The Year of Living Dangerously
    b. The Year of Jubilee
    c. The Year of the Lord
    d. Y2K

20. In the wilderness the Israelites were once attacked by poisonous snakes. God told Moses to put something on a pole so people could look at it and be healed. What was that object?

    a. A cross

    b. A bronze snake

    c. His own sandal

    d. An HMO application

AMAZING FACTS

Both the DeMille classic *The Ten Commandments* and the recent animated movie *Prince of Egypt* assume that Moses and Rameses (the Pharaoh) knew each other growing up. DeMille showed the two as rivals, while the newer film had them as best friends. We don't know from Scripture that they knew each other at all during their adolescence, but it's a pretty good bet. Moses was reared by Pharaoh's daughter as her own, putting him in the royal court of Egypt. A young Rameses would have been growing up at the same time, and he would later succeed his father as pharaoh. But Scripture says nothing about their relationship—whether contentious or congenial—until Moses returned from the desert to say, "Let my people go!"

YOU SAW IT HERE FIRST

Physical Exams

If you go into military service, you need to pass a physical exam. The same was true for God's service in the Old Testament. People with certain defects couldn't serve as priests (Lev. 21:18-20).

The Draft (and draft exemptions)

Young men in the U.S. still need to register for the draft, though it hasn't been an issue for several decades. But back in the 1960s, many were scrambling to be exempted from the draft (or have it deferred) for various reasons.

Ancient Israel also drafted soldiers, but exemptions were allowed for those who had just built a house, planted a vineyard, or gotten engaged (Deut. 20:5-8). Another exemption: "Is anyone terrified? If you are, go home before you frighten anyone else" (Deut. 20:8).

BRAIN STUFF

How can you remember the Ten Commandments? Try these acrostics on for size. You get all the commandments, but not in order.

SHACKLINGS
- **S**abbath
- **H**onor parents
- **A**dultery (don't)
- **C**ovet (don't)
- **K**ill (don't)
- **L**ie (don't)
- **I**dols (don't make)
- **N**ame (of God is holy)
- **G**ods (no other)
- **S**tealing (don't)

But maybe *shacklings* is a bit negative for you. If so, try this word:

OBEDIENTLY
- **O**bserve a day of rest
- **B**e faithful to your spouse
- **E**njoy what you have (don't covet)
- **D**o your parents proud
- **I**dols aren't gods
- **E**steem life
- **N**ame of God is holy
- **T**ake only your own stuff
- **L**ying is wrong
- **Y**ou need to worship God only

CRAZY ADS

Product
Black Sheep Spot Remover
Your flocks will be white as wool. Call our helpful service rep, Jacob.

Service
Shylock Legal Services
When you're falsely accused of assault

Product
Mnemonix

Memory aids so you don't leave any old friends languishing in prison. Tested in Pharaoh's court.

Service
Ammon & Ray Public Relations

When you have a plan that will save the country

Magazine
Better Homes and Dungeons
• How to Become the Warden's Assistant without Losing Your Integrity
• Of Course You Didn't Do It! But No One Cares
• Facing Pharaoh—Preparing Your Appeal
• New Column on Dream Interpretation

Novel
An Israelite Yankee in King Pharaoh's Court

A slave boy crosses cultures to grow up a prince

Product
Manna Helper

Treats for the whole family—in just minutes
(Not suitable for leftovers)

Billboard
Seen in the Sinai Desert:

If you had voted yes, you'd be home by now.

Dumb Jokes

Q: What Israelite singing group did Miriam direct?
A: The Tabernacle Choir

Q: What did Moses do for the headache he got on Mount Sinai?
A: He took two tablets.

Q: What did Israelites say when they sacrificed a sheep?
A: Better ewe than me.

Q: How were the Israelites' worship services in the wilderness?
A: In tents

MINI-QUIZ: FAMOUS FIRSTS

1. Who were the first twins in Scripture (Gen. 25:23-26)?

2. Tubal-cain was a craftsman (Gen. 4:22), the first to work with what material?

3. Naamah, Tubal-cain's sister, was also a "first," though the Bible doesn't mention anything she did. What was she first at?

4. Amazingly, there's no altar mentioned in the accounts of the sacrifices of Cain and Abel. The first altar was built later, by whom?

5. What was the first creature to leave Noah's ark?

QUIZ 3A—3

1. Old Testament Law established certain cities where accused criminals could run to make sure they'd get a fair trial. What were these cities called?
   a. Fair towns
   b. Cities of refuge
   c. City courts
   d. Prisons

2. The Israelites were supposed to give a portion of their crops and flocks to the Lord each year. What portion?
   a. All of it
   b. Half of it
   c. One-tenth of it
   d. Only the first sheaf of corn or animal born

3. **Where was this said? "Let's build a great city with a tower that reaches to the skies—a monument to our greatness! This will bring us together and keep us from scattering all over the world" (Gen. 11:4).**
   a. Eden
   b. Babel
   c. Jerusalem
   d. Manhattan

4. **Who said it? "Will a son be born to a man a hundred years old? Will Sarah bear a child at the age of ninety?" (Gen. 17:17, NIV).**
   a. Methuselah
   b. Abraham
   c. Boaz
   d. The angels of heaven

5. **To protect her family when the Israelites stormed the city, what did Rahab hang out her window?**
   a. A scarlet rope
   b. Her whitest cloak
   c. The fleece of a ewe, sprinkled with dew
   d. Her youngest son

6. **After the Israelites' glorious victory at Jericho, a man named Achan did something wrong that made them lose their next battle. What did he do?**
   a. Gave the enemy their battle plans
   b. Stole some loot from Jericho
   c. Tried to take over leadership from Joshua
   d. Directed *Jericho: The Movie*

7. **There were twelve tribes of Israel, right? But one of them wasn't allotted any land. Which one?**
   a. Levi, because they served as priests for all the tribes
   b. Simeon, because of his crime against Joseph
   c. Benjamin, because it was the smallest tribe
   d. Naphtali, because no one could pronounce it

8. To make up for the landless tribe (see above), the two half-tribes of Manasseh and Ephraim both received land. Which of the sons of Jacob were they descended from?
    a. Reuben
    b. Judah
    c. Joseph
    d. Ernie

9. Gerizim and Ebal are two names associated with a time when the Israelites recommitted themselves to God. What were they?
    a. Two priests who urged Joshua to challenge the people
    b. Two mountains that served as the site for the recommitment ceremony
    c. The two stones on the high priest's breastplate that signaled God's will
    d. The folk-music duo voted best variety act of 1153 B.C.

10. When Ehud killed the obese tyrant King Eglon, what happened to his dagger?
    a. "The dagger vanished because the Lord took it."
    b. "The dagger became white as snow, so Ehud would not take it back."
    c. "The dagger went so deep that the handle disappeared beneath the king's fat."
    d. "The dagger was lost in the evidence room of the Greater Moab Police Department."

11. Sisera found refuge in the tent of Jael, a friend's wife. How did she treat him?
    a. She did his laundry.
    b. She bound his wounds and offered him food.
    c. She gave him a word from the Lord.
    d. She drove a tent peg through his head.

12. **Jephthah made a vow with disastrous results. What did he promise to do if he won the battle?**
    a. To pay his entire fortune to the priest (who turned out to be a crook).
    b. To spare the lives of his enemies. (But they rose up to defeat him.)
    c. To sacrifice the first creature that came out to meet him. (It was his daughter.)
    d. To sing the national anthem before the next battle. (He was tone-deaf.)

13. **From birth, Samson was dedicated to God as a Nazirite. What does that mean?**
    a. He would never drink wine or cut his hair.
    b. He would live with the priest and serve in the tabernacle.
    c. He would study warfare and lead the Israelites in battle.
    d. He lived in Nazareth.

14. **Samson posed this riddle to his enemies: "From the one who eats came something to eat; out of the strong came something sweet" (Judg. 14:14). What was this referring to?**
    a. His own strong-but-sweet personality
    b. His mother bore him after eating some honey.
    c. He had encountered the carcass of a lion in which bees had made honey.
    d. He was test-marketing a new candy bar.

15. **Ruth was the great-grandmother of what Bible hero?**
    a. Moses
    b. David
    c. Esther
    d. The boy who gave his lunch to Jesus

16. **What did the priest think when he saw Hannah praying for a child?**
    a. He thought she was too old to bear children.
    b. He admired her dedication.

c. He wanted her to leave because it was closing time.

d. He thought she was drunk.

17. **Why did the Philistines return the ark of the Lord to Israel after they had captured it?**

    a. They had soldiers hidden inside.

    b. They traded it for the five kings Israel had captured.

    c. Their people were getting sick.

    d. It didn't match the decor in their temple.

18. **In the New Testament, the apostle Paul quoted one of the Ten Commandments, saying it was the first one that ends with a promise. Which commandment did he quote, and what's the promise?**

    a. Do not worship other gods; be true to me and I'll be true to you.

    b. Remember the Sabbath day, and your work will prosper.

    c. Honor your father and mother. Then you will live a long, full life.

    d. Do not lie—people won't believe you when you tell the truth.

19. **Acccording to one of the Ten Commandments, why should we keep the Sabbath Day holy?**

    a. It's the day the world was created.

    b. It's the day with the best weather.

    c. It's the day when the tabernacle is open.

    d. It's the day God took a break from the hard work of creating.

20. **The Year of Jubilee came around for the Israelites once every how many years?**

    a. Seven

    b. Ten

    c. Fifty

    d. One hundred

AMAZING FACTS

The "eye for an eye" command in Scripture (Exod. 21:24) was actually a display of mercy. We often consider it vengeful, but it was actually a way of limiting vengeance. If someone put out your eye or knocked your tooth out, you weren't allowed to kill him.

YOU SAW IT HERE FIRST

Lie Detector?

Scripture mentions a strange method for testing a woman suspected of infidelity. The husband would bring barley flour, which would be burned before the Lord, then mixed with dust and "holy water." The woman would then drink this concoction. If she didn't get sick, she was innocent (Num. 5:11-28).

Building Codes

If you've ever been involved in the construction of a new church building or home, you know the extensive regulations you must follow to bring it "up to code." No one wants injuries that might result from a poorly built house. Well, Old Testament law includes a building instruction for flat-roofed houses—put a barrier around the edge to keep folks from falling (Deut. 22:8).

BRAIN STUFF

First five books of the Bible hard to remember? Think of this silly sentence:

Generation X Loves the Number *Deux*. (*Deux* is French for two.)
Genesis, Exodus, Leviticus, Numbers, Deuteronomy

CRAZY ADS

Sports Headline

Ai, Ai, Sir: Israel Says Next Battle No Problem after a Stunning Upset of Jericho

Tabloid Headline
National Inspirer
Achan Confesses: I Stole Jericho's Loot
—And he's achin' to tell all before he goes underground.

Product
Clubbermaid Jars and Torches
Noiseless . . . for those sneak attacks

Book
When the Vow Breaks
Jephthah's heart-rending story of the oath he lived to regret—but his daughter didn't.

Ad
The Hair Hackery
Strong styles for weak moments
Head stylist: Delilah

Music Video
"I Got You, Babe"
By Hannah and Sam

Dumb Jokes

Q: Why didn't the Israelites take Joshua seriously when he gave them the plan to march around Jericho?
A: They thought he was joshing.

Q: Why wasn't the Jericho woman who hid the spies punished?
A: She was Rahab-ilitated.

Q: What would have happened if Naomi's daughter-in-law had left her?
A: Naomi would have become a ruthless woman.

Q: How was the enemy general Sisera punished after losing to the Israelites?
A: He went to Jael.

Q: How much did Sisera need Jael's help?
A: Like he needed a hole in the head

Q: How did Delilah get into Samson's house?
A: She picked his locks.

Q: How did Samson describe his last date with Delilah?
A: A hair-razing experience

Q: What was Samson's nickname for Delilah?
A: Barber-a

Q: What was it like to serve in Gideon's army?
A: Torcher

TV LISTINGS

Movie of the Week
Midnight in the Garden of Good and Evil
   Boy meets girl. Girl meets snake. Boy keeps girl but loses garden.

Soap Opera
Passion
   She's too old to have a baby, so he takes up with the servant girl,
   who bears a son. The wife kicks mother and son out. Then the
   wife gets pregnant!

Movie of the Week
Mistaken Identity
   Boy meets girl. Boy falls in love with girl. Boy works seven years
   to wed girl. Wrong girl!

Sports
Pro Wrestling
   The Sneak vs. Mystery Man. Jacob's been a tough opponent so
   far, but maybe he'll meet his match.

Movie of the Week
Three Women and a Baby
Mom, Sister, and the Princess of Egypt share the care of this special kid.

Soap Opera
Guiding Light
Will Moses find water in the desert? Will the people take a chance with Caleb and Joshua? Is Miriam coming down with leprosy? Join the Israelites next time on their harrowing trek through the desert.

Movie of the Week
The In-Laws
Mom and daughter-in-law's lives change forever when they meet a ruthless landowner. And what about Naomi?

3B
kings & things

(1 SAMUEL—ESTHER)

QUIZ 3B—1

1. At his coronation, which king was found hiding among the baggage?
   a. David
   b. Joash
   c. Saul
   d. Samsonite

2. What happened when Eli the priest heard the bad news that his sons had died and the ark of God had been captured?
   a. He fell out of his chair and died.
   b. He adopted Samuel as his son.
   c. He cried out with a loud voice, "Why? Why?"
   d. He pretended it never happened.

3. What mistake of King Saul's made God choose another king to replace him?
   a. He violated a peace treaty with the Philistines.
   b. He committed adultery with Bathsheba.
   c. He performed a prebattle sacrifice himself, which only a priest should do.
   d. He kept calling the prophet Samuel "Buster."

4. Eliab, Abinadab, and Shammah weren't right for the job. Who was God's choice?
   a. Joshua (They were other Israelite spies.)
   b. David (They were his older brothers.)
   c. Solomon (They were previous kings not allowed to build the temple.)
   d. Randall Cunningham (They were backup quarterbacks.)

5. What was David doing when he heard Goliath's challenge?
   a. Delivering bread and cheese to the army
   b. Polishing the armor of the soldiers
   c. Tending sheep
   d. Target practice

6. What did the king promise to anyone who killed Goliath?

a. One hundred silver shekels and a post as officer in the army

b. A tax exemption and his daughter's hand in marriage

c. He could keep Goliath's sword and have a song written in his honor.

d. A place in the starting lineup of the Shechem Slingers

7. Why didn't David wear Saul's armor to fight Goliath (1 Sam. 17:39)?

a. It wasn't strong enough to withstand Goliath's sword.

b. He wasn't used to it.

c. He didn't want people to think he was the king.

d. It smelled funny.

8. Finish this lyric of a pop song in Israel: "Saul has killed his thousands . . ."

a. which is why he's the king of the land!

b. but David has killed a giant!

c. and David his ten thousands!

d. and watch out—he'll kill you too!

9. What happened when Saul hurled a spear at David?

a. David caught it and hurled it back.

b. David jumped aside and apparently kept playing the harp for Saul.

c. David died and was miraculously revived.

d. The spear demolished David's harp.

10. How did David's wife help David escape from Saul's soldiers?

a. She bribed them with money from the royal treasury.

b. She put a dummy in bed and said David was too sick to be arrested.

c. She gave him maps that showed where the soldiers were camped.

d. She let him use her private helicopter.

11. **David met someone and "there was an immediate bond of love between them, and they became the best of friends" (1 Sam. 18:1). Who was David's new friend?**
    a. Michal, Saul's daughter
    b. Jonathan, Saul's son
    c. Saul
    d. Joab, Goliath's former bodyguard

12. **Nabal was a wealthy man with a beautiful wife who helped David. What was her name?**
    a. Michal
    b. Bathsheba
    c. Abigail
    d. Mrs. Nabal

13. **Why did David pretend to be crazy?**
    a. So the Philistines would let him live among them for a while
    b. So Saul would stop seeing him as a threat
    c. So he could see whether Absalom would try to seize the throne
    d. He was hoping his subtle portrayal would win him an Oscar.

14. **A man named Uzzah was struck dead. Why?**
    a. He spoke out against King David.
    b. He stole from the loot Israel had taken from the Philistines.
    c. He touched the ark of the covenant.
    d. He was eating too much cholesterol.

15. **How did Nathan get David to see his crime?**
    a. He told him a story about a rich man who stole a poor man's pet lamb.
    b. He sent him a note each day that said, "God knows."
    c. He wrote a psalm of confession.
    d. Hidden video

16. **Two women came to Solomon both claiming to be the mother of a baby. What did Solomon suggest?**
    a. Draw straws
    b. Take a test to determine the best mother
    c. Go to the priest
    d. Cut the baby in half

17. **King Hiram of Tyre (the area of Lebanon) was a loyal friend of David and Solomon. What materials did he supply for the temple?**
    a. Gold
    b. Precious stones
    c. Lumber
    d. Linoleum

18. **How did King Asa die (1 Kings 15:23)?**
    a. A fever
    b. Assassinated by his son Nadab
    c. God smote him
    d. His feet became diseased.

19. **During a famine, Elijah stayed with a widow who was down to her last food. What did he ask her to do?**
    a. Care for her son first
    b. Bake him a bit of bread first
    c. Pray for rain to end the famine
    d. Go on a diet

20. **Elijah mocked the prophets of Baal during the competition at Mount Carmel, suggesting that their god was too busy. Which of the following activities did he *not* mention?**
    a. Sleeping
    b. Traveling
    c. Sending rain
    d. Going to the bathroom

YOU SAW IT HERE FIRST

Heart Attack/Stroke

We're not sure what killed Nabal, but he partied hearty the night before he died, getting really drunk. Then his wife told him that she had decided to help David—over Nabal's objections. In a moment of anger, the Bible says Nabal's "heart failed him," sending him into a coma for ten days, before he finally expired (1 Sam. 25:36-38).

Modern Dance?

Celebrating the joy of bringing back the ark of the covenant to Jerusalem, King David danced along with the procession, wearing a "priestly tunic" and apparently not much else. The queen was not amused. In disgust, Michal complained that "the king . . . exposed himself . . . like any indecent person might do!" (2 Sam. 6:20).

CRAZY ADS

Movie

The Fugitive

A man of the past chases the man of the future. A humble shepherd uses his sheep smarts to evade a vengeful king in the unforgiving caverns of Judea. Starring Saul, David, guest appearance by Jonathan. Features the hit song "Ten Thousands."

"That David is a man after God's own heart."

—Samuel, *Gilgal Gazette*

Magazine

Architectural Digest

• Solomon Has Designs on the Temple: Why David Couldn't Make It Happen

• Waiting in the Wings: Problems with Seraphim Carving

• Pillar Talk

• We Need a New Bezalel!

Music Video

"**Living La Vida Loca**"

King David playing the madman in a Philistine city

Dumb Jokes

Q: Why didn't Saul let the Amalekite king speak?
A: God had Agag order on him.

Q: They called David in from tending his flocks so they could anoint him king. How did he feel about that?
A: Sheepish

Q: What letters of the alphabet were Solomon's favorites?
A: *Y*'s

QUIZ 3B—2

1. **After the widow of Zarephath prepared food for Elijah, what miracle happened?**
   a. Rain poured down from the sky.
   b. She had a continual supply of flour and oil.
   c. Fire came down from heaven, consuming her home.
   d. She invented the microwave oven.

2. **King Ahaziah sent three groups of soldiers to arrest Elijah. What happened to the first two?**
   a. Fire came from heaven to consume them.
   b. They were mysteriously blinded.
   c. They lost their way and never found Elijah.
   d. They became hockey teams.

3. **How did Elisha purify a town's water supply?**
   a. He prayed for spring rains to come early.
   b. He threw salt in it.
   c. He caught the fish that swam in the reservoir.
   d. He bottled it.

4. **The Aramean army surrounded Elisha's village, and they were after Elisha. Elisha's servant was worried as he saw the army, but Elisha asked the Lord to open the servant's eyes. Then what did the servant see?**
   a. Horses and chariots of fire surrounding the Arameans
   b. Clouds on the horizon
   c. The Israelite army ready to attack
   d. All those soldiers in their underwear

5. **When the Aramean army advanced on Elisha, what mysteriously happened to them?**
   a. They started speaking other languages.
   b. They became blind.
   c. Their animals refused to go farther.
   d. They began doing the Macarena.

6. **Whose dead body was eaten by dogs, as Elijah had prophesied?**
   a. Elisha's
   b. Jezebel's
   c. Jehu's
   d. Kibbles

7. **What murderous queen ruled over Judah for seven years?**
   a. Esther
   b. Jezebel
   c. Athaliah
   d. Victoria

8. **When King Hezekiah heard the Assyrian threat, what did he do?**
   a. He gave in to the Assyrian demands.
   b. He sent word to Egypt, asking for help.
   c. He secretly mobilized the armies of the outlying towns.
   d. He prayed.

9. **What sign did God give Hezekiah to assure him of healing?**
   a. His rash went away.
   b. The prophet's wife had a baby boy.
   c. The shadow went backwards on the sundial.
   d. His health insurance was canceled.

10. **After Hezekiah unwisely showed all his palace treasures to envoys from Babylon, what did Isaiah predict?**
    a. Hezekiah would be struck down with illness because of his pride.
    b. The Babylonians would eventually carry all those treasures away.
    c. Hezekiah would marry a Babylonian queen, who would lead him astray.
    d. His holdings would double if he invested in tech stocks.

11. **What king of Judah succeeded his father, Asa, and jumped into an alliance with King Ahab of Israel?**
    a. Omri
    b. Zelepukin
    c. Jehoshaphat
    d. Pippen

12. **King Uzziah went into the temple and burned incense on the altar. What happened then?**
    a. God answered his prayer.
    b. The army suddenly began to win its battle.
    c. He was struck with leprosy because only the priests were allowed to burn incense.
    d. His royal robe caught on fire.

13. **What group of people carried gold bowls and silver utensils with them to Jerusalem?**
    a. The exiled Jews returning from captivity
    b. The Egyptian workers sent by Hiram to construct the temple
    c. The tribe of Dan, seeking peace with the nation of Judah
    d. The First Presbyterian Church on its annual Sunday school picnic

14. After Ezra prayed and confessed the nation's sins, what did the people do?
   a. They cheered and committed themselves to the cause.
   b. They wept bitterly.
   c. They sang a psalm of praise.
   d. They listed all of Ezra's sins.

15. Ezra told the returned exiles, "Now we are even more deeply under condemnation than we were before" (Ezra 10:10). What sin was he most concerned about?
   a. Ignoring the law's hand-washing rituals
   b. Failing to bring tithes to the temple
   c. Intermarrying with local pagans
   d. Chewing gum during the worship services

16. Who was hanged on the gallows he had built for someone else?
   a. Herod
   b. Haman
   c. Mordecai
   d. Ernest Gallo

17. After Jerusalem's wall was rebuilt, there was a great worship service. Ezra read from God's Law; what did the Levites do (Neh. 8:7-8)?
   a. Explained God's Law
   b. Began repairing the wall
   c. Killed their enemies
   d. Sold blue jeans

18. Returning to Jerusalem, what leader arranged for Levites to be paid for their work in the temple, outlawed commerce on the Sabbath, and spoke out against intermarriage with foreigners?
   a. Esther
   b. Nehemiah
   c. Solomon
   d. Pat Robertson

19. **When Mordecai overheard a plot against King Xerxes, what did he do?**
    a. He told his cousin Esther, who told the king.
    b. He killed the two plotters with his sword.
    c. He joined in the planning, hoping to set his people free.
    d. He scolded the plotters for talking too loud.

20. **Haman convinced King Xerxes to kill all the Jews in the kingdom. What was Haman's role in Xerxes' government?**
    a. Keeper of the harem
    b. Xerxes' father and predecessor
    c. Prime minister
    d. Hangman

YOU SAW IT HERE FIRST

Artillery

Long before modern tank warfare, people were inventing battle machines. In Scripture, great King Uzziah is hailed for producing "machines mounted on the walls of Jerusalem, designed by brilliant men to shoot arrows and hurl stones from the towers and the corners of the wall" (2 Chron. 26:15).

CRAZY ADS

Stage Musical

Les MiseraBaals

One honest man leads a revolution against the prophets of a false god

Starring Elijah, Jezebel, and Ahab

Featuring the showstopper tunes:

"Master of the Temple"

"Carmel in the Clouds"

"Bring Him Fire"

Product
"Sons of the Prophets" Tools
 Made with a hollow core, so they'll float. Ax for them at your
 local hardware store.

𝔇𝔲𝔪𝔟 𝔍𝔬𝔨𝔢𝔰

Q: Why was Ezra so eager to get the temple rebuilt?
A: He had an edifice complex.

HIDDEN KINGS

The names of thirteen biblical kings are hidden in the following
nonsense story. Can you find them? (Note: Words and names are
strung between the words of the story.)

As a rule, if I've watched a video twice, it becomes a habit, a kind of
lunacy. Rushing home, I'll watch it with friends or solo, month
after month. It seems like a millennium ago, going to the video
store was fun. Now it's like there's a radar I use to find my favorite
tape. What a dire hobo am I becoming! With eroding willpower, I
struggle to get a grip. Patience is not my strong suit. My brother
Ben had a daily practice. He spoke Navajo as he encouraged me,
and vice versa. Ultimately, we'll win.

Here's what you're looking for:

Agrippa	Herod
Ahab	Joash
Asa	Magog
Ben-hadad	Rehoboam
Cyrus	Saul
Darius	Solomon
David	

TV LISTINGS

Sitcom
Bewitched
> King Saul hits an unhappy medium when he goes to the witch of Endor seeking an audience with Samuel. Guest appearance by . . . Samuel!

Soap Opera
Days of Our Wives
> King Solomon faces challenging cases all day in the throne room, then comes home to his 700 brides. A new drama every day.

Comedy-Drama
Esther McBeal
> A young woman tries to change the world from the royal court of Persia.

3C
the write stuff

(JOB — MALACHI)

QUIZ 3C—1

1. This man, who lived in Uz, was described as "blameless, a man of complete integrity. He feared God and stayed away from evil." Who was he?
   a. David
   b. Hosea
   c. Job
   d. Buzz

2. Which of the following things did *not* happen to Job?
   a. Carthaginian soldiers sowed salt in his fields.
   b. Chaldean warriors stole his camels.
   c. A great wind blew the house down, killing his children.
   d. Fire burned up his sheep.

3. What did Job use to scrape his boils?
   a. A piece of broken pottery
   b. The rib bone of one of his old oxen
   c. The deed to his worthless fields
   d. A brand-new boil scraper

4. What did Job's friends do for the first seven days and nights they spent with him?
   a. Debated the reasons for his woes
   b. Tried to rebuild his house
   c. Sat on the ground with him and said nothing
   d. Rubbed boil-preventing ointment on their bodies

5. What creature is God talking about? It "makes the water boil with its commotion. It churns the depths. The water glistens in its wake. One would think the sea had turned white. There is nothing else so fearless anywhere on earth" (Job 41:31-33).
   a. The crocodile
   b. The whale
   c. The shark
   d. The sea monkey

6. **Jemimah was the name of this man's first daughter—well, after the three who had died. Who was her father?**
   a. David
   b. Jephthah
   c. Job
   d. Noah

7. **Finish this verse: "Kiss the Son . . ." (Psalm 2:12, NIV)**
   a. lest he be angry.
   b. and honor those his people.
   c. and worship him in love and honor.
   d. and give each other holy hugs.

8. **In Psalm 2:4, who is laughing?**
   a. Those who rejoice in the Lord
   b. The Lord, who rules in heaven
   c. The mockers who oppose the faithful
   d. The people who buy this book

9. **Psalm 15 asks, "Who may worship in your sanctuary, Lord?" Which of the following is *not* among the answers?**
   a. Those who lead blameless lives and do what is right
   b. Those who keep their promises even when it hurts
   c. Those who refuse to associate with people of ill repute
   d. Those who do not charge interest on money they lend

10. **What creature does the psalmist compare himself to in Psalm 22:6?**
    a. A dumb ox
    b. A worm
    c. A fool
    d. Herbie, his pet iguana

11. **According to Psalm 40:2 (NIV), "He lifted me out of" what?**
    a. The doldrums of life and gave me a reason to live again
    b. The slimy pit, out of the mud and mire

c. The cistern of the wicked, where there is no peace

d. My fifth-grade Sunday school class

12. According to Psalm 47:1, what should we do with our hands?

a. Lift them up to the Lord

b. Reach out to those less fortunate

c. Clap them

d. Scratch

**13. Finish this verse: "Great is the Lord . . ."
(Psalm 48:1, kjv)**

a. and greatly to be praised.

b. and we praise him with all our hearts.

c. far beyond all human greatness.

d. whithersoever he goeth.

14. In Psalm 73, the psalmist complains about the prosperity of the wicked—until he goes where?

a. To the Lord's sanctuary

b. To the sea

c. To the community of faithful ones

d. To the casino

15. What Israelite leader was the composer of Psalm 90?

a. Joseph

b. Moses

c. Samuel

d. Mendelssohn

16. What majestic bird is used in Psalm 103 as an image of renewed youth?

a. The peacock

b. The raven

c. The eagle

d. The penguin

17. In Psalm 110:1, what piece of furniture would enemies become?

a. A footstool
b. A table
c. A lamp unto my feet
d. A recliner

18. In Psalm 116:1, what reason does the psalmist give for loving the Lord?

a. Because he has created all that is
b. Because he has commanded it
c. Because he hears and answers prayers
d. Because life is so boring when you don't

19. In Psalm 127:4, what weapon are children described as?

a. Arrows in a warrior's hand
b. Swords that divide your heart asunder
c. Catapults that deliver death at a distance
d. Water torture

20. In Psalm 136, what phrase is repeated twenty-six times?

a. Bless the Lord for all his wonderful deeds.
b. His faithful love endures forever.
c. Be righteous in his power.
d. Are we there yet?

AMAZING FACTS

The translators of the King James Version of the Bible tucked a little surprise into Psalm 46, in honor of the great British playwright William Shakespeare (whom some of them probably knew). The forty-sixth word in the psalm is *shake,* and the forty-sixth word from the end is *spear.*

CRAZY ADS

Appeal Letter

Dear friend,

We've all gone through times in life when things have gone bad for us. We thought we'd never get through it, but we did, with the help of our friends. Well, let me tell you about my friend, Job. He's a good guy, but he lost it all. We don't know why he did, but we want to help. That's why a couple of friends and I started the Job Relief Fund. Your tax-deductible contribution will help Job get back on his boil-covered feet.

Dumb Jokes

Q: How do we know God likes to add flavoring to food?
A: "To everything there is a season"

QUIZ 3C−2

1. **Which of the following is *not* mentioned in Psalm 139 as a place where God is present?**
   a. Heaven
   b. The mountaintop
   c. The farthest oceans
   d. The place of the dead

2. **Which of the following are *not* invited in Psalm 148 to praise the Lord?**
   a. All the armies of heaven
   b. Vapors high above the clouds
   c. Believers and unbelievers alike
   d. Fire and hail, snow and storm

3. **The book of Proverbs takes a particular quality and sees it as a person, shouting in the streets and challenging those who live foolishly. What is that quality?**
   a. Righteousness
   b. Worship
   c. Wisdom
   d. Volume

4. Which of the following is *not* listed in Proverbs 6:16-19 as things that the Lord hates?
a. A lying tongue
b. A heart that plots evil
c. A mouth that utters offensive words
d. Feet that race to do wrong

5. Who were King Lemuel and Agur, son of Jakeh?
a. Opponents of King Solomon as he was writing Proverbs
b. Contributors to the book of Proverbs
c. Respectively, the wisest man and most foolish man Solomon knew
d. A comedy team that played the casinos in Tyre and Sidon

6. Which of the following is *not* listed in Proverbs 30:16 as something that is "never satisfied"?
a. The grave
b. The thirsty desert
c. The blazing fire
d. The government

7. Which of the following is *not* listed in Proverbs 30:19 as something "I do not understand"?
a. How an eagle glides through the sky
b. How a snake slithers on a rock
c. How a turtle lives within its shell
d. How a man loves a woman

8. Which of the following is *not* listed in Proverbs 30:25-28 as something "small but unusually wise"?
a. Ants
b. Locusts
c. Lizards
d. Children

9. **The author of Ecclesiastes is often considered to be Solomon—since he was rich, famous, and wise. What name does he go by in this book?**
   a. The Great Experimenter (or Attempter)
   b. The Foolish Sage
   c. The Teacher (or Preacher)
   d. Philip Yancey

10. **According to Ecclesiastes 12:1, when should you remember the Creator?**
   a. In the days of your youth
   b. On the Sabbath day
   c. In times of deep need
   d. While taking Bible quizzes

11. **Finish this verse: "Of making many books there is no end . . ." (Eccles. 12:12, NIV)**
   a. and one person can never learn it all.
   b. and much study wearies the body.
   c. so why even try to read them?
   d. but this book is a really good one.

12. **In chapter 2 of the Song of Songs, which of the following is the young woman *not* compared to?**
   a. The rose of Sharon
   b. The majestic olive tree
   c. The lily of the valley
   d. A lily among thorns

13. **Fill in the blank: "Love is as strong as _____, its jealousy is as enduring as the grave" (Song 8:6).**
   a. the olive tree
   b. a plowing ox
   c. death
   d. garlic

14. **What botanical thing does Isaiah say will come out of "Jesse"—that is, David's family (Isa. 11:1)?**
    a. A flower
    b. A branch or shoot
    c. An olive tree, signifying power
    d. A Chia Pet

15. **According to Isaiah 40:3-5, he heard a voice shouting about making a "highway for the Lord." Where would this highway run?**
    a. Over the hills of Jerusalem
    b. Over the sea to the east
    c. Through the desert
    d. To the mall

16. **In Isaiah 54, who is invited to break forth into song and enlarge her house?**
    a. The mother of the Suffering Servant
    b. A childless woman
    c. Israel
    d. Aretha Franklin

17. **Fill in the blank: "Is anyone thirsty? Come and _____—even if you have no money!" (Isa. 55:1).**
    a. seek the Lord
    b. dine
    c. see this great salvation
    d. drink

18. **Which of the following is *not* one of the Servant's activities listed in Isaiah 61:1-3?**
    a. Bring good news to the poor
    b. Make sinners righteous
    c. Comfort the brokenhearted
    d. Announce that captives will be released

19. **Which of the following is *not* mentioned in Isaiah 65 as a characteristic of the "new earth" God is creating?**
    a. No longer will people be considered old at one hundred.
    b. People will eat the fruit of their own vineyards.
    c. The wolf and lamb will feed together.
    d. Priests and criminals will join in singing praises.

20. **When he wanted Jeremiah to give a message about the Lord's control over his people, where did the Lord tell Jeremiah to go?**
    a. To a shop where a potter worked
    b. To the market where people haggled
    c. To the sea where ships docked
    d. To the skating rink where people went in circles

YOU SAW IT HERE FIRST

Cars?

Reading the King James Version, some people thought Isaiah was talking about cars in 3:18-20. After all, it says how the Lord will take away their "tinkling ornaments . . . and their round tires like the moon, the chains . . . and the mufflers, the bonnets . . ." (bonnet is the British term for a car's hood). But relax. Modern translations make it clear he's talking about the adornment of proud women. Those "round tires like the moon" are probably crescent-shaped necklaces.

Dumb Jokes

Q: King Nebuchadnezzar went crazy and ate grass like a cow. How did he feel?

A: Udderly ridiculous.

QUIZ 3C—3

1. **Jeremiah predicted that what nation would act as God's "deputy," defeating the nation of Judah and taking its people captive for seventy years (Jer. 25:7-11)?**
   a. Egypt
   b. Babylon
   c. Arabia
   d. Luxembourg

2. **What would happened to that conquering nation after those seventy years (Jer. 25:7-11)?**
   a. It would have a revival and know the Lord.
   b. It would become "a desolate wasteland."
   c. It would be conquered by the Jews.
   d. It would wonder where the time went.

3. **Who worked as a scribe for Jeremiah, writing down many of his prophecies?**
   a. Nathan
   b. Baruch
   c. Silas
   d. Jerry Jenkins

4. **In Ezekiel, God compared himself to a certain kind of person when he decided to "search and find" his wandering people (Ezek. 34:11). Jesus used this image for himself later. What type of person was it?**
   a. A priest
   b. A gatekeeper
   c. A shepherd
   d. A bridegroom

5. **Ezekiel gave a message to Gog, the prince of what land?**
   a. Georgia
   b. Magog
   c. Cush
   d. Eggnog

6. **"Mene, Mene, Tekel, Parsin." What's that?**
   a. The first four commandments in Hebrew
   b. The four kings of Canaan who fought Abram
   c. The writing on the wall seen by Belshazzar
   d. The Babylonian Backstreet Boys

7. **Hosea's experiences with his unfaithful wife were an object lesson. What was God's point?**
   a. You can't trust anyone, even those closest to you.
   b. Israel had been unfaithful to God, but he still loved them.
   c. God's holiness is a standard that no human can attain.
   d. Don't get married—ever.

8. **Finish this verse: "Don't tear your clothing in your grief; instead . . ." (Joel 2:13)**
   a. rejoice in the Lord.
   b. tear your hearts.
   c. clothe your tears.
   d. give your old clothes to Goodwill.

9. **Amos just moonlighted as a prophet. His real job was tending sycamore trees and doing what?**
   a. Tending sheep
   b. Serving as scribe to the king
   c. Sailing
   d. Designing Web sites

10. **The prophet Obadiah gave a one-chapter message for which of Israel's neighbors?**
    a. Persia
    b. Edom
    c. Cyprus
    d. Mister Rogers

11. **What enemy city does the prophet Nahum address? (They apparently forgot what Jonah had told them.)**
    a. Athens
    b. Jericho

    c. Nineveh

    d. New York

12. **Which of the following nations did Zephaniah *not* give messages to?**

    a. Philistia

    b. Ethiopia

    c. Rome

    d. Moab

13. **To illustrate his own feelings toward his people, God told Zechariah to take a new job for a while (Zech. 11:4). What job?**

    a. Child care

    b. Shepherd

    c. Soldier

    d. Tax accountant

14. **Zechariah prophesied that something would be "opened" for the people of Jerusalem, "to cleanse them from all their sins and defilement" (Zech. 13:1). What was it?**

    a. A fountain

    b. A cross

    c. A gate

    d. Antibacterial soap

15. **Fill in the blank: "But for you who fear my name, the _____ will rise with healing in his wings" (Mal. 4:2).**

    a. Sun of Righteousness

    b. great bird of freedom

    c. Savior of this world

    d. vitamin doctor

16. Who said it? "Didn't I say before I left home that you would do this, Lord? That is why I ran away to Tarshish! I knew that you were a gracious and compassionate God, slow to get angry and filled with unfailing love. I knew how easily you could cancel your plans for destroying these people. Just kill me now, Lord!"
    a. Jeremiah
    b. Jonah
    c. Jeshua (Joshua) the high priest
    d. Job

17. Which of the following was *not* one of Job's friends who came to comfort him?
    a. Eliphaz the Temanite
    b. Bildad the Shuhite
    c. Jehozaphad the Blusterite
    d. Zophar the Naamathite

18. What prophet had messages for King Ahaz and his son, Hezekiah?
    a. Job
    b. Nathan
    c. Isaiah
    d. Elijah

19. To whom was it said? "Who is this that questions my wisdom with such ignorant words? Brace yourself, because I have some questions for you. . . . Where were you when I laid the foundations of the earth? Tell me, if you know so much."
    a. Moses
    b. Adam and Eve
    c. Job
    d. Charles Darwin

20. What unpopular prophet escaped to Egypt when the Babylonians captured Jerusalem?
   a. Joseph
   b. Jeremiah
   c. Malachi
   d. Agabus

MINI-QUIZ: ISAIAH 40:31

Isaiah 40:31 is one of the great verses of the Bible, an encouragement when you need one. Here are the beginnings of four phrases from that verse. From the collection at the right, select the four appropriate conclusions.

1. But those who wait on the Lord . . .	a. and not faint.
	b. toward my house.
2. They will fly high . . .	c. will find new strength.
3. They will run . . .	d. forever and ever.
4. They will walk . . .	e. will be comforted.
	f. on wings like eagles.
	g. to lofty places.
	h. and not grow weary.
	i. will never be disappointed.
	j. to places of delight.

AMAZING FACTS

The question "Can a leopard change his spots?" was first posed by Jeremiah, who went on to say, "Neither can you start doing good, for you always do evil" (Jer. 13:23).

YOU SAW IT HERE FIRST

Book-Burning

Every so often you'll hear of books being burned in protest against their content. But that's not a new phenomenon. King Jehoiakim hated Jeremiah's negative prophecies so much that he cut up the scroll with a knife and threw the sections in a fire. God just told Jeremiah to write a new scroll (Jer. 36:21-28).

BRAIN STUFF

Need help remembering the minor prophets? Try this mnemonic device:

Holy Joe Aims to Obey Joan. My Neighbor Has Zero Hair and Zebra Markings.

Holy	Hosea
Joe	Joel
Aims	Amos
Obey	Obadiah
Joan	Jonah
My	Micah
Neighbor	Nahum
Has	Habakkuk
Zero	Zephaniah
Hair	Haggai
Zebra	Zechariah
Markings	Malachi

Just imagine living next door to a bald-headed guy who goes to church a lot and wears zebra-skin shirts. He lives with his mother, Joan. It almost makes sense.

CRAZY ADS

Product
Jonah Brand Compasses and Travel Supplies
So you'll never go in the wrong direction again. Also from Jonah—wet suits!

Dumb Jokes

Q: Ezekiel lay on his side for a year and a half to teach the people a lesson. Why didn't they believe him?
A: They thought he was lying.

TV LISTINGS

Drama
The Servant
> Choose to watch this chosen one each week as he proclaims liberty to the captives and sets the prisoners free. This week: He is wounded for the transgressions of others.
> "Completely satisfying!" —Isaiah, *Jerusalem Times*

Sitcom
Friends
Daniel and his three buddies whoop it up in Babylon. This week: They try a new fad diet that the king doesn't like.

3D
good news

(MATTHEW – JOHN)

QUIZ 3D—1

1. What does Emmanuel mean?
   a. Light and life
   b. Good shepherd
   c. God with us
   d. Hallelujah

2. What reason did the angel of the Lord give Joseph for taking Mary and Jesus and fleeing to Egypt?
   a. A great hailstorm was going to destroy Bethlehem.
   b. King Herod was searching for the child to kill him.
   c. The wise men would meet the family in Egypt.
   d. Better weather would be there.

3. What did Herod do when he realized the magi had outwitted him?
   a. He gave orders to kill the magi.
   b. He went into his throne room and stayed for seven days.
   c. He gave orders to kill all the boys in Bethlehem two years old and under.
   d. He burned down the temple.

4. What news did the angel of the Lord bring to Zechariah?
   a. The Romans had overrun Jerusalem.
   b. Jesus had been born in Bethlehem.
   c. He would have a son, who would become a great prophet.
   d. Most Christians in future centuries would forget his name.

5. What did the neighbors and relatives of Zechariah and Elizabeth think they should name their baby?
   a. Zechariah
   b. Joshua
   c. John the Baptist
   d. John the Presbyterian

6. How did Zechariah finally get his voice back?

a. He went to the desert and called upon God.

b. Years later, Jesus healed him.

c. He wrote the baby's name—John—on a tablet, and he could suddenly talk again.

d. He used tongue twisters.

7. Why was Simeon waiting at the temple?

a. He swept the altar area at the end of each day.

b. He was the high priest.

c. He had been told that he wouldn't die until he had seen the Messiah.

d. His buddy Zach had promised to give him a ride home.

8. According to John the Baptist, what should someone with two coats do?

a. Sit far away from the fire

b. Share with one who has none

c. Use one to patch the other

d. Wear a different one each day

9. Who said it? "This Scripture has come true today before your very eyes!" (Luke 4:21).

a. John the Baptist

b. Jesus

c. Mary

d. Gideon

10. Where did John the Baptist begin to preach?

a. The temple colonnade

b. The Judean wilderness

c. The Sea of Galilee

d. Magdalene Square Garden

11. What prophet predicted the coming of John the Baptist?

a. Isaiah

b. Jeremiah

c. Hezekiah

d. Zechariah

12. **What was John the Baptist's purpose?**

   a. To prepare the way for Jesus

   b. To rebuild the temple

   c. To warn the people of Roman domination

   d. To win Wimbledon

13. **Whom did John the Baptist call a "brood of vipers"?**

   a. King Herod

   b. The disciples of Jesus

   c. The Pharisees and Sadducees

   d. The people coming to him for baptism

14. **What did John the Baptist say would happen to every tree that did not produce good fruit?**

   a. It would be thrown into the fire.

   b. It would shrivel from the inside.

   c. It would be left alone until Judgment Day.

   d. It would be made into mangers.

15. **What was Jesus' reply when the tempter tried to convince him to throw himself off the highest point of the temple?**

   a. Man does not live on bread alone.

   b. Why would I want to do that?

   c. Do not test the Lord your God.

   d. You first.

16. **Murder's bad, Jesus said, but what else also deserves judgment (Matt. 5:21–22).**

   a. Adultery

   b. Anger

   c. Apathy

   d. Asparagus

17. **According to Jesus, what's just as bad as committing adultery (Matt. 5:28)?**
    a. Swearing
    b. Drinking
    c. Looking lustfully
    d. Driving with your blinkers on

18. **When you give to someone, what secret should you keep from your left hand?**
    a. What your right hand is doing
    b. How much you're giving or how much is "left"
    c. Why you care so much for that needy person
    d. How to make shadow puppets

19. **How did the hypocrites look when they fasted?**
    a. Holy and pious
    b. Pale and disheveled
    c. Angry and offended
    d. Like they were going to the prom

20. **Fill in the blank: "Your _____ is a lamp for your body" (Matt. 6:22).**
    a. fire
    b. eye
    c. mind
    d. VCR

REMEMBERING THE BEATITUDES

Jesus "blesses" eight types of people in his Sermon on the Mount. You could memorize those eight in order—or you could learn this lovely pair of haikus.

The poor old beggar
apologizes gently
for his loud stomach.

Good Samaritan
unmasks to stop the war
and is killed for it.

The first four beatitudes have to do with our relationship to God. The poor in spirit realize they are just poor old beggars before the Lord. Those who mourn are deeply sorry for their sin. The meek are gentle souls, submitting to the Lord's will for them. The "loud stomach" in the haiku should remind you of hungering and thirsting for God's righteousness. We are blessed when we eagerly desire God's purposes in our lives.

The last four beatitudes deal with our relationship to others. The merciful are "Good Samaritans," helping people in need. Being pure in heart is a matter of taking off our masks, being honest with others about who we are. Peacemakers take chances to stop wars of all kinds, bringing people together. But, of course, some are persecuted for righteousness' sake, even killed in the process.

CRAZY ADS

Product
Frank's Incense
   A present fit for a king

Service
John's Voice Mail
   Prepare the way for the next tech revolution!
   Voice mail that shouts at you—even if you're in the wilderness.

Dumb Jokes

It's the nativity scene. Mary and Joseph are in the stable cradling baby Jesus. Suddenly they hear three voices shouting outside, and then a nine-foot-tall monster with green skin and bolts through his neck comes barging in. One of the voices yells, "I told you to bring Frankin*cense!*"

QUIZ 3D—2

1. **When Jesus sent out his disciples, what group did he tell them to go to (Matt. 10:5-6)?**
   a. The Gentiles
   b. The Samaritans

    c. The lost sheep of Israel

    d. All of the above

2. When Jesus sent out his disciples, how much money were they supposed to take with them?

    a. None

    b. Two shekels for bread and the temple tax

    c. Enough for one week of food and lodging

    d. Five talents

3. Which of the following did Jesus *not* say?

    a. Don't imagine that I came to bring peace to the earth! No, I came to bring a sword.

    b. I have come to set a man against his father, and a daughter against her mother.

    c. If you cling to your life, you will lose it; but if you give it up for me, you will find it.

    d. All things are possible for you if you have clean hands and a pure heart.

4. Why did Jesus denounce the city of Capernaum?

    a. Even though he performed miracles there, they did not repent.

    b. They had allowed Roman soldiers to corrupt their city.

    c. The Pharisees of that city were trying to kill him.

    d. No good Thai restaurants

5. Where do "the wide gate and the broad road" lead?

    a. To pleasure

    b. To destruction

    c. To Jericho

    d. To more wide gates and broad roads

6. Where do the small gate and narrow road lead (Matt. 7:14)?

    a. To life

    b. To the way of peace

    c. To Jerusalem

    d. To a toll booth

7. **How will you recognize false prophets?**
   a. They speak offensive words.
   b. They carry an angry look.
   c. By their "fruit," the way they act
   d. Name tags

8. **Who said it? "Just say the word from where you are, and my servant will be healed! I know, because I am under the authority of my superior officers and I have authority over my soldiers" (Matt. 8:8-9).**
   a. A Roman officer in Capernaum
   b. Nicodemus
   c. The synagogue ruler, Jairus
   d. Simon Peter

9. **Who touched the fringe of Jesus' robe, hoping for healing?**
   a. A Pharisee who was embarrassed to be seen with Jesus
   b. A woman who had suffered with a hemorrhage for twelve years
   c. Peter
   d. Peter's mother-in-law

10. **Where was Jesus going at the time his robe was touched?**
    a. To the temple to teach the scribes
    b. To heal the daughter of a synagogue leader
    c. To chase the money changers from the temple
    d. To the dry cleaners

11. **In the parable of the weeds, what did the farmer decide to do about the weeds growing in his wheat field?**
    a. He immediately pulled up the weeds.
    b. He let the wheat and weeds grow together until harvest.
    c. He burned the entire field.
    d. He used Weed-B-Gone plant-care products.

12. **Whom did Herod the tetrarch think Jesus was?**
    a. God in the flesh
    b. A revolutionary
    c. A simple rabbi who was no threat
    d. John the Baptist, risen from the dead

13. **Jesus conducted a second mass feeding, besides the feeding of the five thousand (Matt. 15:32-39). How many did he feed this time, with seven loaves and a few small fish?**
    a. Four thousand
    b. Three hundred
    c. Seventy
    d. His very hungry disciples

14. **When Jesus talked about the yeast of the Pharisees and Sadducees, what did he mean?**
    a. Their false teaching that added to God's law
    b. Their judgmental spirit that puffed up their own importance
    c. Their ability to talk for hours on a minor point
    d. Their terrible-tasting muffins

15. **Who said it? "It isn't right to take food from the children and throw it to the dogs" (Matt. 15:26).**
    a. Peter
    b. Judas
    c. Jesus
    d. Jairus's daughter

16. **The disciples asked Jesus, "Why couldn't we cast out that demon?" (Matt. 17:19-20). What was his answer?**
    a. "It is a strong foe."
    b. "Let it be for the present."
    c. "You didn't have enough faith."
    d. "There was no demon there to begin with."

17. **Who came to Jesus to ask that her sons sit at his right and left hand in heaven?**
    a. The mother of Zebedee's sons (James and John)
    b. The sister of the centurion Jesus healed
    c. Martha
    d. Elizabeth

18. **Jesus healed two blind men outside of what formerly walled town?**
    a. Jerusalem
    b. Jericho
    c. Capernaum
    d. Detroit

19. **In the parable of the two sons, the first son refused to go to work in the vineyard and later changed his mind and went to work. What did the other son do?**
    a. Ran away from home
    b. Said he would work, but didn't
    c. Tried to keep his brother from working
    d. Watched MTV

20. **Why didn't the chief priests and Pharisees arrest Jesus when he was preaching in the temple?**
    a. They were afraid of the crowds.
    b. They had no evidence to convict him.
    c. They considered the temple sacred space.
    d. He was in disguise.

YOU SAW IT HERE FIRST

Charm Bracelets

Pharisees wore bracelets on their arms—called phylacteries—with Scripture verses inside. Jesus criticized them for "enlarging" these bracelets to show how religious they were (Matt. 23:5). (Ezekiel also warned against the charm bracelets handed out by false prophets—Ezek. 13:18.)

CRAZY ADS

Product
Salt of the Earth

When He reigns, it pours.

𝒟𝔲𝔪𝔟 Jokes

Q: Tradition says that the apostle Peter was the source for the second Gospel. What was Peter's pet name for that book?
A: Mark: my words

Q: Why do people read the third Gospel on cold nights?
A: To be Luke-warm

QUIZ 3D—3

1. **What did John the Baptist say about Jesus' sandals?**
   a. Jesus didn't have to remove them on holy ground.
   b. He (John) was not worthy to stoop down and untie them.
   c. They proved that Jesus was the Chosen One.
   d. They were on sale at Payless.

2. **Why were the people in the synagogue in Capernaum so amazed at Jesus' teaching (Mark 1:22)?**
   a. He used big words.
   b. He taught as one who had real authority, unlike the teachers of the law.
   c. He dared to criticize the religious establishment.
   d. He told them stories.

3. **When Jesus drove out demons, he would not let them speak. Why?**
   a. They knew who he was.
   b. They would fill people's minds with lies.
   c. That was how they regained power.
   d. They sounded funny.

4. **Finish this verse: "The Sabbath was made for man, . . ." (Mark 2:27, NIV)**
    a. the rest of the week for woman.
    b. not man for the Sabbath.
    c. to catch up on weekly chores.
    d. to rest from his labors, as the Creator did.

5. **At one point in Jesus' ministry, the crowds were so large that he and the disciples could not even eat. So his family went to take charge of him. How did they explain their actions (Mark 3:21)?**
    a. We are legally responsible for his actions.
    b. Healthy people don't need a doctor.
    c. Jesus wants to help everyone, but we know he can't.
    d. He is out of his mind.

6. **What was the name of the demon who possessed the man who lived among the tombs of the Gerasenes?**
    a. Terror, because that was its effect
    b. Sin and Death, because that was its goal
    c. Legion, because there were many of them
    d. It had no name.

7. **To whom was it said? "Daughter, your faith has made you well" (Mark 5:34).**
    a. Mary Magdalene
    b. Jairus's daughter
    c. The woman who touched Jesus' cloak
    d. Pollyanna

8. **When Jesus saw the crowd of five thousand who had come to hear him, he had compassion on them because they were like what?**
    a. Unripe fruit on a fig tree
    b. Stones in the desert
    c. Sheep without a shepherd
    d. Hungry teenagers

9. **Why did the disciples want to send the crowd of five thousand away?**
   a. So the people could get something to eat
   b. Because Jesus needed his rest
   c. They were beginning to be unruly
   d. They had to mow the grass

10. **What did the disciples think at first when they saw Jesus walking on the water?**
    a. They thought they were seeing a ghost.
    b. They feared they were already in heaven.
    c. They thought he looked like Peter.
    d. They thought they had run aground in the storm.

11. **What tradition did the Pharisees and teachers of the law notice that the disciples were not holding to?**
    a. Attending Sabbath services
    b. Giving alms to the poor
    c. Ritual hand washing
    d. Stepping over cracks in the sidewalk

12. **Which of the following did Jesus do to heal a deaf and mute man?**
    a. Put his fingers in the man's ears
    b. Spat on his fingers and touched the man's tongue with it
    c. Said, "Be opened."
    d. All of the above

13. **When Peter began to rebuke Jesus for speaking about his coming death, what was Jesus' reply?**
    a. "Get behind me, Satan."
    b. "You will betray me three times."
    c. "You are a loyal friend, Simon."
    d. "Think before you speak."

14. **What were the disciples arguing about on the way to Capernaum?**
    a. The quickest way to get there
    b. Which of them was most important
    c. The meaning of Jesus' teaching
    d. The chances of the Capernaum Chargers in the IFL

15. **Who knows when the events of Matthew 24 will happen?**
    a. Only Jesus' disciples
    b. Those who study the holy Word
    c. The angels in heaven
    d. Only the Father

16. **Who was the chief priest at the time of Jesus' death?**
    a. Lazarus
    b. Nicodemus
    c. Caiaphas
    d. Pontius Pilate

17. **While Jesus was in the home of Simon the leper, what happened that upset his disciples?**
    a. Jesus was arrested by the temple guard.
    b. A woman poured expensive perfume on Jesus' head.
    c. Peter denied Jesus three times.
    d. They began to come down with leprosy.

18. **Finish this verse: "Anyone who is not against us . . ."**
    (Mark 9:40)
    a. might as well be.
    b. is for us.
    c. should help us in our cause.
    d. once they get to know us, they will be.

19. **When Jesus' disciples were criticized for picking grain on the Sabbath, Jesus referred to an Old Testament character who ate the bread that was reserved for priests because he and his men were hungry. Who was that?**
    a. Elijah
    b. Saul
    c. David
    d. Strohmann

20. **In the Great Commission at the end of Matthew, which of the following did Jesus *not* ask his disciples to do?**
    a. Make disciples of all the nations
    b. Baptize them in the name of the Father, Son, and Holy Spirit
    c. Establish churches in every land
    d. Teach people to obey all of Jesus' commands

CRAZY ADS

Product
Bridesmaid Brand Oil Lamps
   With extra oil for those long, lonely nights

Product
Extravagance
   The perfume for that special woman who wants to dazzle a very special man

Video Game
Petris
   Unpack all of the apostle Peter's misdeeds as you try to take his foot out of his mouth.

Dumb Jokes

Q: What do you get when you cross a disciple with a snail?
A: Judas escargot

QUIZ 3D–4

1. John complained that a man was using Jesus' name to cast out demons, but he wasn't one of the disciples (Luke 9:49-50). What did Jesus say about that?
   a. Stop him immediately! He has no right.
   b. Find him and bring him to me. He should become my follower.
   c. Don't stop him! Anyone who is not against you is for you.
   d. Find him and kill him!

2. Jesus told the story of the Good Samaritan in answer to a question. What was the question?
   a. Why should we do good to others?
   b. Who is my neighbor?
   c. How many times should I forgive my brother?
   d. How do you get from Jericho to Jerusalem?

3. Who loved the seats of honor in the synagogue?
   a. Jesus' disciples
   b. The Pharisees
   c. The Roman soldiers
   d. Tax collectors

4. What king did Jesus call a "fox" (Luke 13:31-32)?
   a. Nero
   b. Caesar Augustus
   c. Herod Antipas
   d. Saul

5. What seat should you take at a wedding feast?
   a. The best seat
   b. At the foot of the table
   c. Next to the wine steward
   d. Don't even sit; stand

6. **When you give a banquet, whom should you invite?**
   a. Your friends and relatives
   b. The leaders of society
   c. The poor, the crippled, the lame, and the blind
   d. Someone who can cook

7. **Fill in the blank: "Heaven will be happier over one lost sinner who returns to God than over _____ others who are righteous and haven't strayed away!" (Luke 15:7).**
   a. two
   b. nine
   c. ninety-nine
   d. billions and billions of

8. **In the parable of the Pharisee and the tax collector, why was the tax collector the one who was justified before God?**
   a. He had more money.
   b. He humbled himself.
   c. He called out louder.
   d. He knew someone on the inside.

9. **At Jesus' triumphal entry, the Pharisees asked Jesus to rebuke the crowd for praising him. What did Jesus say?**
   a. "I will for now, but in heaven the angels will still rejoice."
   b. "If they kept quiet, the stones along the road would burst into cheers!"
   c. "You cannot tell me what to do anymore!"
   d. "Who invited you to this party?"

10. **The Jewish leaders asked Jesus for a "miraculous sign" to prove his authority (John 2:18-19). What did he offer?**
    a. Nothing
    b. He turned water to wine.
    c. He said, "Destroy this temple, and in three days I will raise it up" (meaning his body).
    d. He walked on water.

11. **What was the second miracle Jesus performed in Galilee (John 4:43-54)?**
    a. He healed the son of a government official.
    b. He made some of the Pharisees unable to speak.
    c. He provided food for the disciples to carry on their journey.
    d. He turned wine back into water.

12. **What is the name of the pool near the Sheep Gate in Jerusalem where the invalids would gather, waiting for an angel to stir up the water?**
    a. Bethesda
    b. Bathsheba
    c. Beersheba
    d. The Waiting Pool

13. **Who said it? "Lord, to whom would we go? You alone have the words that give eternal life" (John 6:68).**
    a. Jesus
    b. Peter
    c. Jairus
    d. Herod

14. **To whom was it said? "Satan has asked to have all of you, to sift you like wheat. But I have pleaded in prayer for you . . . that your faith should not fail" (Luke 22:31-32).**
    a. Judas Iscariot
    b. Jesus
    c. Simon Peter
    d. Pontius Pilate

15. **Jesus' disciples asked, "Was it a result of his own sins or those of his parents?" (John 9:2). What are they talking about?**
    a. A famous builder dying when a tower collapsed
    b. A man being born blind
    c. The wickedness of Pontius Pilate
    d. Peter's habit of wearing clothes that clashed

16. **Who said it? "He is old enough to speak for himself.
Ask him" (John 9:20–21).**
    a. Parents of the formerly blind man, being grilled by authorities
    b. Mary, when the steward asked her to get Jesus to make more wine
    c. The rabbis in the temple, when Mary asked them where young Jesus had been
    d. Herod's wife, when her daughter asked what he wanted for his birthday

17. **What did Jesus say to the fig tree that had no fruit?**
    a. "May no one ever eat your fruit again!"
    b. "A better day is coming for all of us."
    c. "You are as evil as the tree in Eden!"
    d. "Your bark is worse than your bite."

18. **Jesus was being grilled with tough questions, so he
launched one of his own. He asked the religious leaders
whether John the Baptist was sent from God or just
acting on his own. How did they answer?**
    a. From God, and the people revere him as a prophet.
    b. On his own, but baptizing was a very clever idea.
    c. He was offensive and unwashed; we want no part of him.
    d. We don't know.

19. **Jesus told a story of a vineyard owner who leased the
field and sent servants to collect the rent. The first two
servants were beaten and sent back. What happened to
the third servant?**
    a. He was beaten even worse.
    b. He was killed.
    c. He was paid the rent.
    d. He was hired to stomp the grapes.

20. **After Jesus told this parable, the leaders wanted to arrest
Jesus. Why didn't they?**
    a. It was the Sabbath day.
    b. They were afraid of the crowds.

c. That would be like admitting the parable was about them.

d. Jesus slipped away before they could.

CRAZY ADS

Product
Whitewashed Tombs
    They look great!
    (If you don't mind the stench)

Invitation
You're Invited . . .
    . . . to the king's wedding feast.
    Sorry for the short notice—the original invitees couldn't make it.

Product
Bethesda Hot Tubs and Saunas
    You'll swear it was stirred up by an angel

Dumb Jokes

Q: How did the landowner feel after paying all his workers for their hours of picking grapes?

A: Di-vine.

HIDDEN NT PEOPLE

The names of thirteen New Testament people are hidden in the following story. Can you find them? (Note: Names are strung between the words of the story.)

I hope terrible things don't mar your plans. Let me take those thoughts back and reword them into better ones. I must admit I'm bitter, since the flu kept me from a much needed vacation. Now I'm at the worst point. It used to be better, but now I can't keep my spirits up. I lately have listened to music, becoming quite the audiophile. Months ago, I called the radio station and left the DJ a message to play a certain disc. A riot ensued. I just don't want any tragedy or other odious event to mar that trip of yours.

Here's what you're looking for:

Andrew	Matthew
Herod	Onesimus
Iscariot	Peter
James	Philemon
Luke	Pilate
Martha	Titus
Mary	

QUIZ 3D—5: PASSION WEEK

1. Jesus cried out from the cross, *"Eloi, Eloi, lema sabachthani"*; what does this mean?

    a. "I offer my body as a sacrifice for sin."

    b. "My God, My God, why have you forsaken me?"

    c. "Only Elijah can comfort me now."

    d. "Into your hands I commend my spirit."

2. On the cross, Jesus was offered what beverage on a sponge?

    a. Sour wine

    b. Sour milk

    c. Milk mixed with wine

    d. Muddy water

3. What was torn in two at the moment Jesus died?

    a. The high priest's robe

    b. The curtain in the temple

    c. The seamless garment the soldiers had gambled for

    d. The stone tablets of the Law

4. Who said it? "Surely not I?" (Matt. 26:22, NIV).

    a. Joseph of Arimathea, when Jesus spoke of his burial

    b. Pontius Pilate, when challenged by the chief priests

    c. Each of Jesus' disciples, when Jesus said one of them would betray him

    d. Mary Magdalene, when Jesus announced he would rise and appear to someone

5. **What orders did Pilate give to make Jesus' tomb secure?**
   a. He had Jesus buried in a secret location.
   b. He had a trench built around the tomb and filled it with water.
   c. He had a seal put on the stone door and posted a guard.
   d. He had Jesus' disciples followed.

6. **A mob armed with swords and clubs approached Jesus, following Judas. Where were they?**
   a. On the shores of Galilee
   b. The Garden of Gethsemane
   c. The road to Calvary
   d. By the well of Samaria

7. **Jesus told some disciples to take a donkey's colt for his triumphal entry into Jerusalem. What were they supposed to say if someone challenged them about taking the colt?**
   a. The Lord needs it and will return it soon.
   b. This is very important business.
   c. This colt is the chosen fulfillment of Zechariah's prophecy.
   d. We're from the government.

8. **Those standing near the cross thought Jesus was calling out to whom?**
   a. His mother
   b. Elijah
   c. Pilate
   d. John the Baptist

9. **What was Barabbas in prison for?**
   a. Teaching people to break the Sabbath
   b. Insurrection and murder
   c. Insulting a centurion
   d. Robbing the temple treasury

10. **Why didn't the women prepare Jesus' body for burial the day after his crucifixion?**
    a. Roman law required a day of waiting.
    b. The guards wouldn't let them.

    c. It was the Sabbath.

    d. In their grief, they hadn't gathered the necessary spices.

11. Who said it? "What is truth?" (John 18:38).

    a. Herod

    b. Pilate

    c. Jesus

    d. John

12. When the risen Jesus met Mary in the garden, whom did she think he was?

    a. Peter or John

    b. A gardener

    c. An angel

    d. Adam

13. During the last week before his crucifixion, Jesus spent his days preaching at the temple. Where did he spend his nights?

    a. On the Mount of Olives

    b. In Bethlehem

    c. Still preaching at the temple

    d. Meeting with Nicodemus

14. Who dragged in a net with 153 large fish before having breakfast with Jesus?

    a. James and John

    b. Peter

    c. Mark

    d. Martha

15. The risen Jesus met two disciples on the road to what town?

    a. Bethlehem

    b. Jericho

    c. Emmaus

    d. Damascus

16. **What did the apostles think when the women came back from the tomb, talking about resurrection?**
    a. They were excited.
    b. They remembered Jesus' prophecies.
    c. They were afraid the story would bring repercussions from the authorities.
    d. They thought it was nonsense.

17. **What did Peter see when he peered into Jesus' tomb (Luke 24:12)?**
    a. Nothing
    b. Empty linen wrappings
    c. Dazzling light
    d. An angel chorus

18. **What was Pilate's reaction to the crowd's cries to crucify Jesus?**
    a. He washed his hands and declared he was innocent of Jesus' blood.
    b. He grabbed the whip and used it on Jesus.
    c. He sent a letter of protest to the emperor.
    d. He had the crowd's ringleaders arrested.

19. **What did the governor's soldiers dress Jesus in as they mocked him?**
    a. A white Roman toga
    b. Tarnished armor and a "spear" made of papyrus
    c. A scarlet robe, a crown of thorns, and a staff in his right hand
    d. A leather tunic with a camel's hair cloak

20. **What does "Golgotha" mean?**
    a. The Place of the Skull
    b. Crucifixion Hill
    c. Hill of Shame
    d. Place of the Gentiles

AMAZING FACTS

A Christian sect in Ethiopia honors Pontius Pilate as a hero of the faith, claiming that he converted after sentencing Jesus. There's no valid historical evidence to prove that.

CRAZY ADS

Product
Innocence Hand Soap
Endorsed by Governor Pilate

Web Site
www.fish.net
Count the catch with Simon Peter

TV LISTINGS

Drama
H.Y.P.O. Blue
Follow the exploits of the hypocritical Pharisees and their legal experts. Watch them open loopholes and close them—catching sinners in the act.

Sitcom
All in the Family
Mrs. Zebedee tries to gain special places in God's kingdom for her boys, James and John. The Thunder Boys try to call fire down from heaven while Dad mends his nets.

Cable Channel
The Weather Channel
The latest news on that strange calm that suddenly stopped the storm on the Sea of Galilee.

Movie of the Week
Silence of the Lamb
He is arrested, tried, convicted, but he opens not his mouth.

3E
church chat

(ACTS—REVELATION)

QUIZ 3E—1

1. **What did the eleven remaining disciples decide to do about the position of the twelfth one, Judas?**
   a. They would wear patches on their tunics in memoriam.
   b. They would select another disciple to take his place.
   c. They would choose seven new disciples.
   d. They would start calling themselves apostles.

2. **Some people thought Jesus' disciples were drunk. When?**
   a. When Peter and John preached in the temple, despite being warned not to
   b. When they held their joyous meetings in the middle of the temple
   c. When they spoke in tongues at Pentecost
   d. When they kept trying to turn water into wine

3. **Which of the following was *not* a point that Peter made in his Pentecost speech (Acts 2)?**
   a. That Jesus' miracles meant he had come from God
   b. That Jesus' miraculous birth had been announced by angels
   c. That Jesus had fulfilled Old Testament prophecy
   d. That his hearers, along with the Romans, were responsible for Jesus' death

4. **Who encountered a lame man begging at the Beautiful Gate of the temple (Acts 3:2)?**
   a. Jesus
   b. The eleven apostles
   c. Peter and John
   d. Kathy Ireland

5. **When the religious leaders interrogated these people, they "could see that they were ordinary men who had had no special training. They also recognized them as men who had been with Jesus" (Acts 4:13). Who were they?**
   a. Peter and John
   b. Paul and Titus
   c. Matthias and Joseph Barsabbas
   d. Nicodemus and Joseph of Arimathea

6. **Ananias and Sapphira brought an offering to the apostles and were struck dead. Why?**
   a. They had brought grain rather than a sacrificial animal.
   b. They had lied about how much they were giving.
   c. They had grumbled against the apostle Peter.
   d. They hadn't properly deducted it on their tax statements.

7. **An expert named Gamaliel (guh-MAY-lee-el) gave the Jerusalem authorities some good advice about dealing with the Christians. What did he say?**
   a. Crush the movement now, or you'll be sorry later.
   b. This movement will never amount to anything, so ignore it.
   c. Leave them alone—Christianity will only grow if God is behind it.
   d. Christians serve the best tuna casseroles.

8. **Stephen was arrested and falsely charged by the Jewish authorities. What was he charged with?**
   a. Starting a rebellion
   b. Blasphemy
   c. Breaking the Sabbath
   d. Jaywalking

9. **In Samaria, a man named Simon was fascinated by the apostles' power to touch people with the Holy Spirit. In fact, he offered them money to gain this power. What was his profession before he became a Christian?**
   a. Blacksmith
   b. Sorcerer
   c. Sea captain
   d. Computer technician

10. **To whom was it said? "Do you understand what you are reading?" (Acts 8:30).**
   a. Jesus, with rabbis in the temple
   b. The Ethiopian eunuch, in the desert with Philip
   c. Pilate, in conversation with Herod
   d. The Corinthians, in Paul's epistle

11. **Who said it? "Saul! Saul! Why are you persecuting me?" (Acts 9:4).**
   a. Peter, in a Jerusalem jail
   b. Barnabas, arguing over their second journey
   c. Jesus, in a vision from heaven
   d. David, in the Judean desert

12. **According to Romans 4:9, who was "declared righteous by God because of his faith"?**
   a. Adam
   b. Abraham
   c. John the Baptist
   d. Paul

13. **Fill in the blank: "So now there is no _____ for those who belong to Christ Jesus" (Rom. 8:1).**
   a. condemnation
   b. sorrow
   c. pleasure
   d. sin

14. **Who "prays for us with groanings that cannot be expressed in words" (Rom. 8:26)?**
    a. The church
    b. The Holy Spirit
    c. The saints of ages past
    d. Our mothers

15. **According to Romans 13:10 (NIV), what is the fulfilling of the law?**
    a. Righteousness
    b. Sacrifice
    c. Love
    d. Study

16. **Who were the different groups in Corinth following?**
    a. Paul, Peter (Cephas), Apollos
    b. Jesus, Baal, Zeus
    c. Isis, Mithra, Ashtarte
    d. James, John, Barnabas

17. **Finish this verse: "No eye has seen, no ear has heard, no mind has imagined . . ." (1 Cor. 2:9)**
    a. the power of God in the life of one who obeys him.
    b. what God has prepared for those who love him.
    c. the deep destruction caused by ignoring God's word.
    d. the future glory awaiting those who help themselves.

18. **Finish this verse: "Everything is permissible for me, but not everything is . . ." (1 Cor. 6:12, NIV)**
    a. allowed.
    b. beneficial.
    c. caring.
    d. delightful.

19. **Why does Paul say he does not deserve to be called an apostle (1 Cor. 15:9)?**
    a. Because he continues to struggle with sin
    b. Because he wasn't one of the original Twelve

c. Because he once persecuted the church of God

d. Because his hair isn't long enough

20. **Fill in the blank: "If Christ was not raised, then all our preaching is _____" (1 Cor. 15:14).**

a. all the more important

b. boring

c. useless

d. brilliant

BRAIN STUFF

Forgetting the order of Paul's epistles in the New Testament? Learn this sentence, and you'll have the first letter of each book:

Reading **C**ritical **C**orrespondence **G**ets **E**ach of **P**aul's **C**hurches **T**hinking **T**hat **T**imeless **T**ruth **T**ransforms **P**eople.

Reading	**R**omans
Critical	1 **C**orinthians
Correspondence	2 **C**orinthians
Gets	**G**alatians
Each (of)	**E**phesians
Paul's	**P**hilippians
Churches	**C**olossians
Thinking	1 **T**hessalonians
That	2 **T**hessalonians
Timeless	1 **T**imothy
Truth	2 **T**imothy
Transforms	**T**itus
People	**P**hilemon

Want more? All right! The remaining New Testament letters can be remembered with this sentence:

Heavenly **J**esus **P**ersuades **P**eople to **J**ust **J**oin **J**esus' **J**oyous **R**evolution.

Heavenly	Hebrews
Jesus	James
Persuades	1 Peter
People (to)	2 Peter
Just	1 John
Join	2 John
Jesus'	3 John
Joyous	Jude
Revolution	Revelation

CRAZY ADS

Magazine
Waiting Tables
• Being the Best Deacon You Can Be
• What's Up with These Grecian Widows?
• Philip's Guide to Desert Wear
• You Can Still Speak Out—even if you're just an administrator

Product
Prophet-on-Tape

Wouldn't it be nice to have someone pop out of nowhere to explain Scripture to you? Like that's ever gonna happen! But now the explanation is right here on this enhanced Scripture CD. Send check or money order to Candace Court, Ethiopia.

QUIZ 3E—2

1. The two candidates were Joseph Barsabbas and Matthias. Matthias won. What did he win?

    a. A position as one of the twelve disciples, replacing Judas

    b. The right to record the memoirs of the apostles

    c. The role of head deacon in the early church

    d. The early church's first table tennis championship

2. **Who was "walking, leaping, and praising God" in Solomon's Colonnade?**
   a. Peter
   b. The lame man healed by Peter and John
   c. David
   d. Rhoda

3. **The authorities warned Peter and John not to preach about Jesus. What happened next?**
   a. They prayed with other Christians.
   b. The house where the Christians met was shaken.
   c. Peter and John kept preaching.
   d. All of the above

4. **What physical problem did Saul have after his experience on the Damascus Road?**
   a. He limped.
   b. He couldn't speak.
   c. He couldn't see.
   d. He looked just like his twin brother.

5. **After Saul's conversion, the Jewish authorities in Damascus were out to kill him. How did he escape the city?**
   a. In disguise, at night
   b. In a cart carrying pigs to market
   c. In broad daylight
   d. In a basket, over the city wall

6. **A Christian woman named Tabitha was "always doing kind things for others and helping the poor" (Acts 9:36). She'd even make coats and clothing for people. What was her Greek name?**
   a. Alexandra
   b. Priscilla
   c. Dorcas
   d. Jezebel

7. **Where was Peter when messengers from Cornelius the centurion arrived at his house?**
   a. Meditating on the roof
   b. Resting by the seaside
   c. Preaching in the temple
   d. Fighting the Visigoths

8. **Which apostle was first to be killed for his faith?**
   a. James
   b. John
   c. Luke
   d. Peter

9. **In the town of Lystra, some out-of-towners stirred up trouble and stoned Paul. He was dragged out of the city, given up for dead. Then what happened?**
   a. The believers mourned for three weeks after sending his body back to Tarsus.
   b. Barnabas went on to Cyprus with John Mark.
   c. Paul got up and went back into the city.
   d. All of the above

10. **Acts 15 records a council meeting where the Jerusalem church leaders met with missionaries Barnabas and Paul to discuss church policy. What was the main issue?**
    a. Whether they should continue to collect money from the churches they visited
    b. Whether Gentile believers should be required to convert to Judaism
    c. Whether they should take the gospel west of Rome
    d. Whether to reprimand the youth minister for his crazy antics

11. **Before going on a second missionary journey, Paul and Barnabas split up. What was the issue?**
    a. Barnabas wanted to take Mark with them; Paul didn't.
    b. Barnabas wanted to go to Cyprus; Paul wanted to go to Rome.

    c. Both wanted to be the main speaker of the group.

    d. Barnabas thought Paul had bad breath.

12. In 1 Corinthians, Paul spoke harshly against a church member who was acting scandalously. What does he say in 2 Corinthians about him?

    a. Haven't you thrown him out of the church yet?

    b. Be careful that he doesn't influence the rest of you with his sin.

    c. Now it's time to forgive him and comfort him.

    d. You'd better make peace with him before he sues you.

13. What everyday vessels did Paul compare our bodies to (2 Cor. 4:7, NIV)?

    a. Wooden rowboats

    b. Pitchers of water

    c. Jars of clay

    d. Tupperware

14. In Galatians, Paul tells of a time he confronted Peter and criticized him. What had Peter done?

    a. Exalted himself as leader of the church

    b. Refused to eat with Gentiles when the legalists were present

    c. Taught false things about Jesus

    d. Forgot to take Paul fishing

15. Finish this verse: "For we are God's workmanship, created in Christ Jesus . . ." (Eph. 2:10, NIV)

    a. to do good works, which God prepared in advance for us to do.

    b. for his pleasure, which we seek daily.

    c. to praise him and fail him, to cling to his grace.

    d. to display the glories of his creative spirit.

16. According to 1 Thessalonians 4:16, what sound will accompany the Lord's return?

    a. A commanding shout

    b. The call of the archangel

c. The trumpet call of God

d. All of the above

17. According to 1 Timothy 2:8, who should "pray with holy hands lifted up to God, free from anger and controversy"?

a. Men

b. Women

c. Children

d. Pro wrestlers

18. Paul told Timothy to tell certain people "not to be proud and not to trust in their money" (1 Tim. 6:17). Who was that message for?

a. The Galatians

b. The false teachers

c. Those who are rich in this world

d. Fashion models

19. God has not given us a spirit of timidity, but of what (2 Tim. 1:7)?

a. Power

b. Love

c. Self-discipline

d. All of the above

20. According to Titus 3:5, why did God save us?

a. Because of the good things we did

b. Because of his mercy

c. Because of our sins

d. All of the above

CRAZY ADS

Hit Song

"Up on the Roof"

By Simon Peter and the Centurions

Service

Damasket Basket Travel Services

When you really have to get out of town . . . tonight!

MINI-QUIZ: FAMOUS FIRSTS

1. Who was the first Christian martyr?

2. What was the occasion when Jesus performed his first miracle?

3. Barnabas was one of the first foreign missionaries. Who was the other one?

4. In Antioch, the followers of Jesus began to be known by a certain term. What was it?

5. Which of Jesus' disciples was first to be killed for his faith (though his brother lived the longest)?

QUIZ 3E—3

1. In Damascus, God told a believer named Ananias to go to a house on Straight Street to meet whom?
   a. Peter
   b. The Lord
   c. Saul (Paul)
   d. His future wife

2. Mark was the cause of the split between Paul and Barnabas. Why?
   a. He insisted on winning every argument.
   b. He was a Gentile.
   c. He had abandoned them, going home early during their first journey.
   d. He kept throwing spitballs.

3. **What was the name of the first Christian convert in Philippi—"a merchant of expensive purple cloth" (Acts 16:11-15)?**
   a. Luke
   b. Lydia
   c. Loretta
   d. Hilfiger

4. **To whom was it said? "Believe on the Lord Jesus and you will be saved, along with your entire household" (Acts 16:31).**
   a. Cornelius the centurion
   b. Saul, who became known as Paul
   c. A jailer in Philippi
   d. Lydia, at the Philippian riverbank

5. **What "eloquent speaker" arrived in Ephesus from Alexandria and was instructed by Priscilla and Aquila?**
   a. Apollos
   b. Barnabas
   c. Pliny the Younger
   d. Alexander

6. **During a revival in Ephesus, people brought their magic books and did what to them?**
   a. Tore them to pieces
   b. Rewrote them
   c. Burned them
   d. Made them disappear

7. **Demetrius was upset because Paul's preaching had reduced the demand for silver shrines of the local deity. So he gathered people of his profession to start a protest march. What profession did Demetrius have?**
   a. Police officer
   b. Philosopher
   c. Silversmith
   d. Spy

8. **Who said it? "It is more blessed to give than to receive" (Acts 20:35).**
   a. David
   b. Jesus
   c. Barnabas
   d. Jude

9. **A prophet named Agabus took something of Paul's and bound his own feet and hands with it, predicting that Paul would be bound and delivered to the Romans. What did he take?**
   a. Paul's belt
   b. Paul's tie
   c. Paul's knapsack
   d. Paul's staff

10. **Paul was arrested by Jewish authorities in the Jerusalem temple. What did they say he had done?**
    a. Taken God's name in vain
    b. Blasphemed the temple by bringing a Gentile inside
    c. Stolen from the money changers
    d. Brought unclean foods into the temple

11. **After being arrested in Jerusalem, how did Paul avoid being whipped by Roman soldiers?**
    a. By sneaking out during the night
    b. By convincing them of the truth of the gospel
    c. By stealing the whip
    d. By declaring his Roman citizenship

12. **A queen named Bernice heard the apostle Paul give a defense of his faith. Who was her husband?**
    a. Festus
    b. Agrippa
    c. Caiaphas
    d. Peter

13. **According to Hebrews 4:16 (NIV), what should we "approach . . . with confidence"?**
    a. The throne of grace
    b. The confession booth
    c. Church leadership
    d. All of the above

14. **What should we "run with endurance" (Heb. 12:1)?**
    a. The ministries of the church
    b. The course through the desert
    c. The race God has set before us
    d. The treadmill of life

15. **What is "pure and lasting religion in the sight of God our Father" (James 1:27)?**
    a. Caring for widows and orphans
    b. Refusing to let the world corrupt us
    c. Both of those
    d. Neither of those

16. **Who was "as human as we are, and yet when he prayed earnestly that no rain would fall, none fell for the next three and a half years!" (James 5:17)?**
    a. Moses
    b. Elijah
    c. Daniel
    d. Peter

17. **Who "personally carried away our sins in his own body" (1 Pet. 2:24)?**
    a. Adam
    b. Moses
    c. Christ
    d. all of the above

18. **According to 1 Peter 3:15, what should we "always be ready" to do?**
    a. Give an answer to those who ask the reason for our hope
    b. Do good deeds to show our true loyalty
    c. Help those who are suffering persecution
    d. Fill in for the pastor

19. **Who is "greater than the one who is in the world" (1 John 4:4, NIV)?**
    a. You
    b. The one who is in you
    c. The apostle John
    d. Your minister

20. **Which of the following is *not* one of the seven churches receiving the book of Revelation?**
    a. Ephesus
    b. Corinth
    c. Thyatira
    d. Philadelphia

YOU SAW IT HERE FIRST

Appealing to a Higher Court

People who aren't satisfied with a court's ruling can often appeal to a higher court. The same sort of thing happened in Roman times. A Roman citizen charged with a crime could "appeal to Caesar" and face an imperial court in Rome. Paul used this on a fairly minor "disturbing the peace" charge, which he probably could have beaten (Acts 24). But he had an ulterior motive: He got a military escort to Rome, where he wanted to preach the gospel.

CRAZY ADS

Magazine
Business Woman
Woman of the Year: Lydia of Thyatira

Read her purple prose about the clothing market and the new
direction in her life

Extra feature on tentmaker/teacher Priscilla

Product
Silver Shrines by Demetrius
Artemis of the Ephesians and all other local deities
Going out of Business Sale!

News Headline
Council OKs Gentiles but Suggests a Few Guidelines
Paul, James Both Claim Victory
Peter Hails Compromise Measure

Dumb Jokes

Q: How do we know God is a coffee drinker?
A: He brews.

Q: Why did the Romans expect Paul to serve them drinks?
A: He'd spent a lot of time behind bars.

HIDDEN NT PLACES

The names of twelve New Testament places are hidden in the
following story. Can you find them? (Note: Names are strung
between the words of the story.)

After work, I drone on about this gal I leer at. No, actually I just
admire the decor in the office where she works. I think her name is
Beth. Anyway, the walls have pictures of local varying scenes—a
barn, a silo, a mule-drawn cart, a hacienda, then some more of the
flora and fauna in the area—an ox, a burro. Me, I'm no artist, just a
poet. I still remember every lit test passed, every exam aced on
iambic pentameter, or some such stuff. But Beth doesn't care. She
has a boyfriend, and I know I could be in major danger if I don't
watch my step. He suspects nothing so far.

Here's what you're looking for:

Athens	Jordan
Bethany	Kidron
Calvary	Macedonia
Corinth	Nain
Ephesus	Rome
Galilee	Siloam

TV LISTINGS

Soap Opera
As the World Learns
Paul wants to go back to Asia Minor, but he won't take Mark. Barnabas has other plans. Will their ministry get back on track?

Tragi-comedy
The Honeymooners
Ananias and Sapphira have done it this time—*both* lying to the church about their contributions. See what trouble they get into this time. Final episode!

Comedy
Happy Days
The Philippians are cruising as they heed Paul's advice: "Rejoice in the Lord *always*." (You can say that again!) This week: Clement helps Euodia and Syntyche sort out their differences.

Drama
Corinthian Hope
An apostle shows a better way to a church in turmoil.

News Extra
Evangelism Tonight
Latest reports on missionary activity. How's Paul getting along with his new team? What's happening with Barnabas and Mark on Cyprus? Will Apollos ever get his act together?

Drama

Law and Other

Paul takes on the legalists, who insist that salvation depends on keeping the law. Paul argues powerfully for God's grace. Don't miss it!

3F
mix it up

(GENERAL INFORMATION)

QUIZ 3F—1

1. **What structure was 450 feet long, 75 feet wide, and 45 feet high?**
   a. The tabernacle
   b. Noah's ark
   c. The chariot that took Elijah to heaven
   d. The table at the Last Supper

2. **When was it said? "Do not hurt the boy in any way, for now I know that you truly fear God. You have not withheld even your beloved son from me."**
   a. When the angel kept Abraham from sacrificing his son Isaac
   b. When Joseph kept his brothers from striking Benjamin
   c. Samuel stopped Jesse from punishing young David for staying in the fields
   d. Dr. Spock was writing his first child-care book

3. **The Lord said "The sons in your womb will become two rival nations." To whom was he talking, and about whom?**
   a. To Eve, about Cain and Abel
   b. To Rebekah, about Jacob and Esau
   c. To Elizabeth, about John the Baptist
   d. To Solomon, about the divided kingdom of Israel and Judah

4. **Who said it and to whom? "Don't be angry with yourselves that you did this to me, for God did it."**
   a. Jesus to Judas
   b. David to Saul
   c. Joseph to his brothers
   d. Jonah to the whale

5. **Which of the following is *not* a language that the Bible was originally written in?**
   a. Greek
   b. Hebrew

    c. Arabic

    d. Aramaic

6. **To whom was it said? "Who appointed you to be our prince and judge? Do you plan to kill me as you killed that Egyptian yesterday?"**

    a. Pharaoh

    b. Jesus

    c. Julius Caesar

    d. Moses

7. **Which of the following cities was *not* visited by Paul?**

    a. Antioch

    b. Athens

    c. Alexandria

    d. Berea

8. **To whom was it said? "Who gave man his mouth? Who makes him deaf or mute? Who gives him sight or makes him blind? Is it not I, the Lord? Now go; I will teach you what to say" (Exod. 4:11, NIV).**

    a. Moses, after he complained that he was not a skilled speaker

    b. Elijah, depressed after his great victory at Mount Carmel

    c. Simon Peter, after he complained to Jesus

    d. Young Timothy, before his school play

9. **Besides Psalms, which book of the Bible has the most words?**

    a. Leviticus

    b. Jeremiah

    c. Malachi

    d. Concordance

10. The song begins, "I will sing unto the Lord, for he has triumphed gloriously; he has thrown both horse and rider into the sea." What was the occasion?
    a. David won an important battle against the Philistines.
    b. The Babylonian army returned home without sacking Jerusalem.
    c. The Israelites passed through the Red Sea, and the Egyptians didn't.
    d. King Herod had a little rodeo mishap at his seaside palace.

11. Which of the following biblical items have archaeologists found?
    a. Joseph's coat
    b. David's lyre
    c. Hezekiah's tunnel
    d. Leftovers from the feeding of the five thousand

12. Who said it? "What if there are fifty righteous people in the city? Will you really sweep it away and not spare the place for the sake of the fifty righteous people in it?" (Gen. 18:24, NIV).
    a. Enoch
    b. Abraham
    c. Lot
    d. Jonah

13. What group did these three men belong to? Jashobeam, who killed 300 enemies in one battle; Eleazar, who fought Philistines in a barley field; Benaiah, who killed a lion in a snowy pit
    a. David's "mighty men"
    b. Daniel's associates as leaders in Babylon
    c. Moses' advisors in the wilderness
    d. The NRA

14. **Who said it? "I will not let you go unless you bless me"
(Gen. 32:26, NIV).**
    a. Jacob, to the mysterious being he wrestled with
    b. Esau, after Jacob stole his father's blessing
    c. Martha, after the raising of Lazarus
    d. Goliath, to David

15. **Who said it? "Here I am living in this beautiful cedar
palace, but the Ark of the Lord's covenant is out in a
tent!" (1 Chron. 17:1).**
    a. Joshua
    b. David
    c. Jeremiah
    d. Noah

16. **To whom was it said? "I have heard your prayer and
seen your tears. I will heal you. . . . I will add fifteen
years to your life, and I will rescue you and this city
from the king of Assyria" (2 Kings 20:5-6).**
    a. Isaiah
    b. Hezekiah
    c. Ahab
    d. Rip van Winkle

17. **After Psalms, which book of the Bible has the most
chapters?**
    a. Proverbs
    b. Matthew
    c. Isaiah
    d. Obadiah

18. **After Psalms, which book of the Bible has the most
verses?**
    a. Genesis
    b. Numbers
    c. 1 Corinthians
    d. Hymnal

19. **Who said it to whom? "Please send a letter to Asaph, the manager of the king's forest, instructing him to give me timber. I will need it to make beams for the gates of the Temple fortress."**
    a. Nathan to King David
    b. Isaiah to King Ahaz
    c. Nehemiah to King Artaxerxes
    d. Columbus to King Ferdinand

20. **To whom was it said? "Why did you ever take us out of Egypt? Why did you bring us here? We, our children, and our livestock will all die!" (Exod. 17:3).**
    a. Moses
    b. Joseph's brothers
    c. The angel who spoke to Joseph, the husband of Mary
    d. Northwest Airlines

YOU SAW IT HERE FIRST

Addicted to Love

King Saul's daughter Michal was "in love" with David and they married, but they had a rocky relationship, largely due to Saul's developing hatred of David. Samson "fell in love with" Delilah, the original femme fatale. He told her that the secret of his great strength was in his hair, and she betrayed him. Let's just say he was dis-tressed.

Dumb Jokes

Hollywood, Part 1

Q: If Hollywood did a musical about Esther's relationship with Xerxes, what would it be called?
A: *The King and I*

Q: If Hollywood did a movie about Paul's evangelical travels, what would it be called?
A: *Witness*

Q: If Hollywood told the story of God making Eve from Adam's ribs, what would it be called?

A: *While You Were Sleeping*

Q: What would Hollywood title a movie about Noah's ark?

A: *Animal House*

Q: If Hollywood did a film about the magi visiting Jesus, what would it be called?

A: *Three Wise Men and a Baby*

MINI-QUIZ: ANAGRAMS

1. What prophet's name could be reformed to spell A RICH HAZE?

2. With all the dreams and manifestations of God's presence in this book, it may be appropriate that its letters can also spell SEEINGS.

3. The letters of this book could be reformed to spell CIVIL SUET. I know that's "suit" misspelled, but actually suet—fat—does appear in this book, in sacrifices.

4. Appropriately, this can be respelled ONE MORE DUTY.

5. This history book gives us 2 RICH CLONES.

6. This prophet could be HUMAN.

7. After new legislation, this guy was NAILED. I just hope he wasn't in DENIAL.

8. This man's name can be rearranged to spelled A SHOE, which might be what he felt like throwing at his wife.

QUIZ 3F–2: FEAR NOT

To whom were these reassurances made?

1. "I am the God of your father, Abraham. . . . Do not be afraid, for I am with you and will bless you. I will give you many descendants, and they will become a great nation. I will do this because of my promise to Abraham, my servant" (Gen. 26:24).
   - a. Isaac
   - b. Ishmael
   - c. Joseph
   - d. David

2. "I am God, the God of your father. . . . Do not be afraid to go down to Egypt, for I will make you into a great nation there. I will go down to Egypt with you, and I will surely bring you back again. And Joseph's own hand will close your eyes" (Gen. 46:3-4, NIV).
   - a. Isaac
   - b. Jacob
   - c. Judah
   - d. Samuel

3. "Do not be afraid; do not be discouraged. Take the whole army with you, and go up and attack Ai. For I have delivered into your hands the king of Ai, his people, his city and his land" (Josh. 8:1, NIV).
   - a. Moses
   - b. Joshua
   - c. Saul
   - d. Gideon

4. "Do not be afraid. Go and tell my brothers to go to Galilee; there they will see me" (Matt. 28:10, NIV).
   - a. Peter
   - b. Paul
   - c. The women who came to anoint Jesus' body
   - d. The soldiers who stood guard at the tomb

5. "Don't be afraid; from now on you will catch men" (Luke 5:10, NIV).
   a. Simon Peter
   b. James and John
   c. Matthew (Levi)
   d. Paul (Saul)

6. "Do not be afraid; keep on speaking, do not be silent" (Acts 18:9, NIV).
   a. Moses
   b. Samuel
   c. The Samaritan woman
   d. Paul

7. "Do not be afraid. I am the First and the Last. I am the Living One; I was dead, and behold I am alive for ever and ever! And I hold the keys of death and Hades" (Rev. 1:17–18, NIV).
   a. Isaiah
   b. Ezekiel
   c. Luke
   d. John

8. "Do not be afraid . . . your prayer has been heard. Your wife Elizabeth will bear you a son, and you are to give him the name John" (Luke 1:13, NIV).
   a. Elkanah
   b. Zechariah
   c. Joseph
   d. Titus

9. "Do not be afraid. I bring you good news of great joy that will be for all the people" (Luke 2:10, NIV).
   a. Soldiers
   b. Shepherds
   c. Magi
   d. Writers

10. **"Do not be afraid . . . , you have found favor with God. You will be with child and give birth to a son" (Luke 1:30-32, NIV).**
    a. Hannah
    b. Esther
    c. Mary
    d. Lydia

AMAZING FACTS

The Bible has shaped several languages of the world, including English. Christian missionaries brought the Latin Scriptures to England and taught the locals to read—thus replacing the ancient rune symbols with the Latin alphabet. A millennium later, several new Bible translations (including the King James Bible) helped to standardize the English language. Elsewhere, missionaries Cyril and Methodius translated the Scriptures into Slavic languages—and in the process created the Cyrillic alphabet that those languages still use. As late as the twentieth century, it was Bible translators who taught many primitive tribes to read and write their own languages.

Dumb Jokes

Hollywood, Part 2

Q: If Hollywood did a movie based on Jonah sailing for Tarshish instead of going to Nineveh, what would the title be?

A: *Whale of Two Cities*

Q: If Hollywood told the story of David killing Goliath and cutting off his head, what would the movie be called?

A: *Sling Blade*

Q: What would Hollywood call a movie about the tornado that whipped through Job's hometown?

A: *The Wizard of Uz*

Q: What would Hollywood call a movie that had Peter with a speech impediment, saying, "You mutht be thaved!"
A: *Apostle Lisps Now*

Q: What would Hollywood call a political sit-com about Sodom and Gomorrah?
A: *Sin City*

MINI-QUIZ: GIFTS GIVEN

1. **Who gave his son a "coat of many colors" (Gen. 37:3, KJV)?**
   a. Abraham
   b. Jacob
   c. Joseph
   d. Calvin Klein

2. **Who gave her son back to God, to serve in the tabernacle (1 Sam. 1:11)?**
   a. Jochabed
   b. Hannah
   c. Naomi
   d. Esther

3. **What woman gave Solomon gold, spices, and precious gems?**
   a. Bathsheba
   b. The daughter of Pharaoh
   c. The queen of Sheba
   d. Jezebel

4. **To whom did Mary give a jar of expensive perfume, sort of?**
   a. Judas
   b. Jesus
   c. Peter
   d. Lazarus

5. **Who gave David a robe, tunic, sword, bow, and belt?**
   a. Jonathan
   b. Solomon
   c. Bathsheba
   d. Goliath

QUIZ 3F–3: MOUNTAINS

Many important events occurred on mountains. See if you can fill in the details of the following "mountaintop experiences."

1. **What vessel came to rest on Mount Ararat?**

2. **Who nearly killed his son on Mount Moriah?**

3. **On what mountain did Moses receive God's law?**

4. **Who died on Mount Nebo, overlooking the land he'd been seeking for forty years?**

5. **The Israelites recommitted themselves to God between the mountains of Ebal and Gerizim. Who led this revival?**

6. **What female judge led Israel to victory near Mount Tabor?**

7. **Who challenged the prophets of Baal at Mount Carmel?**

8. **What king danced with the procession that led the ark of the covenant up to Mount Zion?**

9. **Who preached the Sermon on the Mount?**

10. **What prophet moped in a cave on Mount Horeb, fearing for his life?**

AMAZING FACTS

The book *Ben-Hur* came out of an argument about the Bible. Lew Wallace was debating with a skeptical friend—and losing. In frustration he went home and determined to write a story that would show the truth of his belief in Jesus. The result was this classic Christian novel (and film).

MINI-QUIZ: WEDDINGS

1. Jacob thought he was marrying his beloved Rachel. Who was actually under the veil?
   a. Leah
   b. Ruth
   c. Deborah
   d. Laban

2. What man gave a seven-day wedding feast, riddled his guests, got upset, and killed thirty people?
   a. Lot
   b. Samson
   c. Goliath
   d. Arnold

3. What scribe urged the Jews returning from exile to divorce their foreign wives?
   a. Baruch
   b. Ezra
   c. Malachi
   d. The rich young ruler

4. Jesus turned water to wine at a wedding feast in what city?
   a. Canaan
   b. Cain
   c. Cana
   d. K–mart

5. Jesus told of a king who prepared a great wedding feast for his son (Matt. 22:1-14). Why did the king get upset?
   a. The people he invited didn't come.
   b. The son called off the wedding.
   c. The food was second-rate.
   d. The dry cleaners lost his tux.

6. In another story Jesus told, five bridesmaids were prepared for a wedding ceremony and five weren't. What didn't the unprepared ones have?
   a. Formal clothing
   b. Food for the banquet
   c. Dates
   d. Oil for their lamps

7. The Bible speaks of the "wedding feast of the Lamb," at which Jesus will wed his bride, the church. In what book would you read about this?
   a. Exodus
   b. Daniel
   c. Revelation
   d. The Late Great Planet Earth

QUIZ 3F—4: DREAMERS

1. Who dreamed of a stairway from earth to heaven (Gen. 28:12)?

2. Who had a dream of fat cows and skinny cows that meant famine for his land (Gen. 41)?

3. Who had a dream telling them *not* to go back to Jerusalem (Matt. 2:12)?

4. Whose dreams annoyed his brothers (Gen. 37:5)?

5. Who dreamt of a man from Macedonia calling, "Come over here and help us!" (Acts 16:9)?

6. Who had a dream in which God offered him anything he wanted (1 Kings 3:5)?

7. The Babylonian king had a fitful dream, but he couldn't even remember it. He demanded that his advisors tell him what he dreamt and what it meant. Who was able to do it (Dan. 2)?

8. Who had a dream telling him to go ahead and marry his scandal-ridden fiancée (Matt. 1:20)?

9. Cornelius the centurion had a vision telling him to send for what apostle (Acts 10:3-6)?

10. Joel prophesied that "your old men will dream dreams. Your young men will see visions" (Joel 2:28). When did Peter quote this psalm (Acts 2)?

11. Who had a dream of four huge beasts: a lion with wings, a bear, a four-headed leopard, and another vicious one with ten horns (Dan. 7)?

12. A woman had a nightmare that convinced her Jesus was innocent. She was the wife of what official (Matt. 27:19)?

13. Ananias had a vision telling him to go and meet what new believer (Acts 9:10-16)?

14. A butler and a baker had dreams that meant one would die, the other would live. Who interpreted their dreams (Gen. 40)?

15. A soldier had a dream in which a loaf of bread rolled down a hill and demolished the camp of the enemy

Midianites. This dream predicted the victory of what outmanned general (Judg. 7:13)?

16. What odd prophet had a dream in which he saw the glory of God's rebuilt temple (Ezek. 43)?

17. "When the Lord restored his exiles to Jerusalem, it was like a dream!" In what book of the Bible would we find that lyric?

18. Who had a rooftop vision of a sheet with unclean foods (Acts 10:9-16)?

AMAZING FACTS

Portions of the Bible have been translated into more than 2,000 languages. In the year 1800, only 68 languages had even portions of Scripture.

Recently the Arts and Entertainment Network, in cooperation with various scholars, named their most important people of the millennium. Who ranked No. 1? A German named Johannes Gutenberg, who invented the printing press. What did he print? Bibles. There are 48 known copies of Bibles printed by Gutenberg still in existence. Each is worth millions of dollars.

QUIZ 3F—5: FIND THE BOOK

What book would you turn to if you wanted to find . . .

1. **The Sermon on the Mount**
   a. Deuteronomy
   b. Matthew
   c. 1 Thessalonians
   d. *Preaching for Fun and Prophet*

2. **"God is love."**
   a. Deuteronomy
   b. 1 Corinthians

    c. 1 John

    d. *Love Story*

3. The fruit of the Spirit

    a. Ezekiel

    b. John

    c. Galatians

    d. *The Grapes of Wrath*

4. Three men thrown in a furnace

    a. Genesis

    b. Daniel

    c. 2 Corinthians

    d. *Fahrenheit 451*

5. "Don't let anyone think less of you because you are young."

    a. Esther

    b. Mark

    c. 1 Timothy

    d. *Don't Sweat the Small Stuff*

6. A prophet thrown into a pit

    a. 2 Kings

    b. Jeremiah

    c. Acts

    d. *Catch-22*

7. "The wages of sin is death."

    a. Romans

    b. Genesis

    c. Revelation

    d. *Gone with the Wind*

8. A prophecy about Bethlehem as the birthplace of a king

    a. Exodus

    b. Micah

    c. Luke

    d. *A Tale of Two Cities*

9. A new heaven and a new earth
    a. Psalms
    b. Matthew
    c. Revelation
    d. *Brave New World*

10. Two people struck dead for lying to the church
    a. 2 Kings
    b. Acts
    c. Jude
    d. *Left Behind*

11. "Not by force, nor by strength, but by my Spirit, says the Lord."
    a. Zechariah
    b. 2 Samuel
    c. Ephesians
    d. *Atlas Shrugged*

12. The Prodigal Son
    a. Amos
    b. Luke
    c. Hebrews
    d. *Men Are from Mars*

13. A nighttime talk with Nicodemus
    a. Nehemiah
    b. Jeremiah
    c. John
    d. *A Night to Remember*

14. Paul's shipwreck
    a. Matthew
    b. Acts
    c. Titus
    d. *Titanic*

15. Dry bones
> a. Ezekiel
> b. Judges
> c. Proverbs
> d. *Jurassic Park*

16. "For all have sinned; all fall short of God's glorious standard."
> a. Genesis
> b. John
> c. Romans
> d. *Heart of Darkness*

17. A man in a den of lions
> a. Judges
> b. Daniel
> c. Revelation
> d. *The Hiding Place*

18. The Love Chapter
> a. Job
> b. John
> c. 1 Corinthians
> d. *True Romance*

19. The Faith Chapter
> a. Hebrews
> b. Matthew
> c. Romans
> d. *The Power of Positive Thinking*

20. "Faith without works is dead."
> a. Mark
> b. 1 Corinthians
> c. James
> d. *Ragtime*

21. "All of us have strayed away like sheep."
a. Psalms
b. Isaiah
c. Philippians
d. *The Call of the Wild*

22. A prisoner who becomes prime minister
a. Genesis
b. Ezra
c. Malachi
d. *Horatio Alger*

AMAZING FACTS

How many Bible women find their names in Oscar-winning films?

Three and a half. Eve appears twice—in *All about Eve* (1950) and *Three Faces of Eve* (1957). Bette Davis won for *Jezebel* in 1938, and *Rebecca* (forgive the misspelling of Rebekah's name) won best picture in 1940. The half? Shirley Booth in 1952 for *Come Back Little Sheba* (as in "queen of").

Other Oscar-winning films with biblical titles are:

• *East of Eden* (1955)—"and Cain went out from the presence of the Lord, and dwelt in the land of Nod, on the east of Eden" (Gen. 4:16, KJV).
• *Lilies of the Field* (1963)—"Consider the lilies of the field, how they grow" (Matt. 6:28, KJV).
• *Chariots of Fire* (1981)—"And the Lord opened the eyes of the young man and he saw: and, behold, the mountain was full of horses and chariots of fire round about Elisha" (2 Kings 6:17, KJV).
• *Tender Mercies* (1983)—"Remember, O Lord, thy tender mercies and thy lovingkindnesses" (Ps. 25:6, KJV, and many other psalms).

Dumb Jokes

Hollywood, Part 3

Q: What would Hollywood call a TV show about Jacob's wresting match?

A: *Touched by an Angel*

Q: What would Hollywood call a cable show about the confusion of languages at the Tower of Babel?

A: *Talk Soup*

Q: What would Hollywood call cable programming about a curious Pharisee?

A: *Nic(odemus) at Nite*

Q: What would Hollywood call a movie about Lazarus rising from the dead?

A: *Heaven Can Wait*

Q: What would Hollywood call God's flooding Pharaoh's army in the Red Sea?

A: *Chariots of Mire*

and finally . . .

Q: What would Hollywood call a TV show about why it's smart to follow God's will?

A: *Father Knows Best*

answers

QUIZ 1A—1

1. b. In the beginning God created the heavens and the earth.
2. c. God
3. a. He rested
4. a. People
5. c. God
6. b. The garden in which Adam and Eve lived
7. c. Eat the fruit of the tree of the knowledge of good and evil
8. a. Adam
9. c. The serpent
10. d. Abel
11. b. Killed him
12. b. Cain
13. b. Noah
14. b. A boat that held animals
15. b. There was going to be a major flood.
16. b. Rain
17. c. A rainbow
18. d. A skyscraper that touched the heavens
19. a. God told him to
20. c. The land Abraham moved to

QUIZ 1A—2

1. b. Abraham
2. a. Twin sons of Rebekah
3. d. A bowl of stew
4. b. He used goatskin to make his arms seem as hairy as Esau's.
5. c. He wanted to kill Jacob.
6. b. On a stairway to heaven
7. c. A multicolored coat
8. d. All of the above
9. c. Basket made of reeds
10. b. Pharaoh's daughter
11. b. Sharks
12. b. The death of all firstborn sons in Egypt
13. a. Bread, which they called manna
14. b. Forty years

15. a. God gave them the Law.
16. b. Honor them
17. c. Golden jewelry the people wore
18. c. Do not strike your brother in retaliation.
19. b. Stone tablets
20. c. A pillar of cloud by day, a pillar of fire by night (Num. 14:14)

MINI-QUIZ: FAMOUS FIRSTS
1. Pharaoh (Gen. 40:20)
2. Noah (Gen. 9:20-21)
3. Sarah (Gen. 20:2-8)
4. Abraham (Gen. 23:3-20)
5. Rachel (Gen. 29:9)

QUIZ 1A—3
1. b. Esau
2. b. The Moabites
3. c. Twelve
4. c. The Egyptian who bought Joseph as a slave
5. b. Jericho's walls fell down.
6. c. Hezekiah
7. c. Shamgar
8. d. Pitchers, trumpets, and torches
9. a. A bush was burning, but didn't burn up.
10. a. Tola, Jair, and Jephthah
11. b. Ruth and Orpah
12. b. Gideon
13. b. The Egyptians were killing all the Israelite baby boys.
14. c. Ruth (Ruth 1:16)
15. a. Give it right back
16. b. Eli was the priest who raised Samuel.
17. d. Samuel
18. b. He heard a voice calling him.
19. b. Let my people go!
20. d. March around the city every day for a week

QUIZ 1B—1

1. b. Saul
2. b. David
3. c. Solomon
4. c. Samuel
5. b. Played the harp
6. c. Goliath
7. b. A slingshot
8. a. Because Saul was still God's anointed king.
9. c. Jerusalem
10. b. Jonathan, son of Saul
11. b. The ark of the covenant was being brought to Jerusalem
12. c. Bathsheba
13. c. He sent Uriah to the army's front lines and had the army pull back.
14. c. Nathan
15. c. Goliath
16. b. Absalom
17. b. Solomon
18. b. Wisdom
19. b. The queen of Sheba
20. c. Judah

QUIZ 1B—2

1. b. Jezebel
2. b. Elijah
3. c. Omri, Ahab, Jehu
4. b. Drought
5. c. Mount Carmel
6. a. Jehoshaphat, Hezekiah, Josiah
7. b. Solomon
8. b. Baal
9. b. Elijah
10. a. Elijah's sacrifice was consumed by fire.
11. b. Elisha
12. b. Afraid that the queen would hunt him down and kill him.

13. b. A chariot of fire appeared, and a whirlwind took Elijah to heaven.
14. c. Elijah's cloak
15. b. Leprosy
16. a. He was angry that Elisha didn't greet him personally.
17. a. Nothing
18. b. Babylon
19. b. The temple
20. b. Idol worship, rejection of God

QUIZ 1B—3
1. c. Hezekiah
2. b. Elijah
3. b. Held a weapon
4. d. He prayed.
5. b. David
6. b. Because he was a warrior and had shed much blood.
7. a. The golden angels in the temple's Most Holy Place
8. b. The ark of the covenant was brought to the temple.
9. c. Elijah
10. b. Solomon
11. d. Solomon
12. c. The queen of Sheba
13. b. Solomon
14. b. Asa
15. b. King Cyrus of Persia
16. a. Ezra
17. c. Esther
18. b. Elisha, Obadiah, and Balaam
19. d. All of the above
20. c. Ezra

QUIZ 1C—1
1. a. Satan
2. a. Because God had protected him and made him rich.
3. b. Boils

4. b. You must have done something to deserve all this. (C is close, so give yourself half credit for that.)
5. a. God can do whatever he wants.
6. b. Job's goods were restored by twice as much, and he got ten more children.
7. b. Those who do not dance with immoral people
8. d. David
9. c. what is man that you are mindful of him?
10. b. Fools
11. b. The heavens and the skies
12. b. forsaken me?
13. c. I shall not want.
14. c. In green meadows (pastures)
15. b. Through the dark valley of death
16. c. Goodness and mercy
17. c. and know that I am God.
18. c. whiter than snow.
19. a. The Lord
20. b. go into his courts with praise.

QUIZ 1C—2
1. b. Blessed
2. b. As far as the east is from the west
3. c. we will rejoice and be glad in it.
4. b. lamp, light
5. b. In his heart
6. a. "Let us go to the house of the Lord."
7. a. test me and know my thoughts.
8. b. Preaching
9. b. Solomon
10. c. 150
11. b. the beginning of knowledge.
12. a. do not depend on your own understanding.
13. b. Anger or wrath
14. c. She teaches her children from her own knowledge.
15. b. but you surpass them all.
16. b. "Lord, I'll go. Send me!"

17. d. They flew.
18. b. God is with us.
19. b. child/son
20. c. Ruler of All Flesh

MINI-QUIZ: SEASONS
1. c. and a time to die
2. n. and a time to harvest
3. f. and a time to heal
4. l. and a time to rebuild
5. a. and a time to laugh
6. k. and a time to dance
7. b. and a time to gather stones
8. g. and a time to turn away
9. m. and a time to lose
10. d. and a time to throw away
11. j. and a time to mend
12. i. and a time to speak up
13. e. and a time to hate
14. h. and a time for peace

QUIZ 1C—3
1. c. A sacrificial lamb
2. b. rejected/sorrows
3. b. Jeremiah
4. c. Daniel (Dan. 6:22)
5. a. Jerusalem
6. c. consumed, compassions, morning, faithfulness
7. b. Joseph, and later Daniel
8. b. Jonah (Jon. 1:2)
9. c. Writing on the wall
10. b. whirlwind
11. c. Jonah
12. b. In large, clear letters so even the messenger could read it and tell everyone
13. b. Daniel (Dan. 5:15–16)
14. b. The temple

15. b. Amos and Joel
16. c. my house lies in ruins?
17. c. A donkey
18. c. scattered
19. b. A messenger
20. c. Malachi

QUIZ 1D—1

1. a. Mary
2. a. Gold, frankincense, and myrrh
3. a. Gabriel
4. d. She would become pregnant with Jesus.
5. d. It would never end.
6. b. impossible
7. c. Elizabeth's baby, in her womb
8. b. Caesar Augustus
9. c. Bethlehem
10. c. A manger, used to feed cattle
11. c. An angel of the Lord
12. c. The Word
13. c. flesh
14. b. The Jordan River
15. b. A dove
16. a. Forty days and forty nights
17. b. The devil
18. b. Caesar
19. c. Love the Lord your God with all your heart, all your soul, and all your mind.
20. c. Love your neighbor as yourself.

QUIZ 1D—2

1. b. Curse God and die
2. c. chosen
3. b. Twelve
4. a. Rock
5. a. On a stand
6. c. Talking with Jesus on the Mount of Transfiguration

7. a. Lays down his life
8. a. Mary, Martha, and Lazarus
9. a. Simon Peter and Andrew
10. c. Fishermen
11. c. They will be filled.
12. a. light
13. b. "Turn the other cheek" so you might get hit again.
14. c. Love them and pray for them.
15. b. In heaven
16. b. Solomon
17. d. Remove the plank from your own eye
18. b. They were afraid they would drown in the storm.
19. a. A paralyzed man healed by Jesus
20. c. Tax collector

MINI-QUIZ: SEEDS AND SOILS

1. c. Birds ate the seeds.
2. b. Plants sprang up, then wilted.
3. d. Plants were choked.
4. a. Produced a bigger crop than was planted.

QUIZ 1D—3

1. a. Stones into bread
2. b. sheep, wolves
3. c. light
4. c. A pearl
5. c. Five loaves and two fishes
6. b. Peter
7. a. Simon Peter
8. c. Their cross
9. c. little children
10. b. Leave the ninety-nine to look for the one
11. b. Go through the eye of a needle
12. c. first
13. a. They will be humbled.
14. b. the greatest.
15. b. Jesus

16. c. and the truth will set you free.
17. c. In Cana in Galilee
18. c. find
19. a. A priest and a Levite
20. c. Hunt down the robbers

QUIZ 1D—4

1. b. Jesus' baptism
2. c. They made an opening in the roof and lowered the man down.
3. a. It cannot stand.
4. b. The disciples were afraid in a terrible storm.
5. c. In his hometown
6. a. King Herod had him beheaded.
7. b. his soul.
8. c. Dazzling white, whiter than anyone in the world could bleach them
9. a. Gouge it out
10. b. To serve
11. c. to God what is God's.
12. a. Two small copper coins
13. b. It was all she had.
14. c. Before the rooster crowed
15. a. A lost coin
16. b. No place to lay his head
17. c. Let the dead bury their own dead.
18. a. Mary and Martha
19. c. They ran out of wine, so Jesus turned some water into wine.
20. c. Be merry

QUIZ 1D—5

1. c. Daily bread
2. a. Into temptation
3. b. Sitting at Jesus' feet, listening to him teach
4. b. The hairs on our heads
5. b. Taking care of pigs
6. d. All of the above

7. c. He was angry and jealous.
8. b. masters
9. c. Lazarus
10. a. Be born again
11. b. So much that he gave his only Son
12. b. Living water
13. b. life.
14. b. A woman captured in the act of adultery
15. a. The devil
16. b. Mary and Martha
17. c. He climbed up a tree.
18. a. He washed their feet.
19. c. The Counselor, or Comforter—the Holy Spirit
20. b. The branches (John 15)

QUIZ 1D—6: PASSION WEEK

1. b. Palm branches
2. c. A donkey
3. a. Gethsemane
4. b. The Last Supper
5. b. The stone was rolled back, and the angel of the Lord was sitting there.
6. d. "Crucify him!"
7. a. "Today you will be with me in paradise."
8. a. In a new tomb carved out of rock
9. b. body.
10. b. Peter
11. a. they don't know what they are doing.
12. b. To anoint the body with spices for burial
13. c. His pierced hands and side
14. b. Thomas
15. c. He returned the priests' money and hanged himself.
16. a. Pontius Pilate
17. b. He gave Jesus a kiss of greeting.
18. c. This is Jesus, the King of the Jews.
19. c. Joseph of Arimathea
20. a. Thomas

QUIZ 1E—1

1. b. power, witnesses, ends
2. c. Jesus had just ascended into heaven.
3. b. At the day of Pentecost, when the Spirit filled the disciples
4. a. People from different nations understood them in their own languages.
5. a. Pentecost (Acts 2:41)
6. c. Healing
7. b. Peter and the apostles
8. b. Stephen
9. a. He was stoned to death.
10. c. That Philip should baptize him
11. b. Saul
12. c. The first Gentile to become a Christian
13. b. Peter
14. b. gospel.
15. d. All of the above
16. c. Death
17. c. Paul
18. a. Your body
19. c. love.
20. b. a new creation; the old has gone, the new has come!

QUIZ 1E—2

1. c. Saul
2. c. An angel
3. d. Peter
4. c. Barnabas and Saul
5. b. Barnabas and Paul
6. a. Paul
7. c. Timothy
8. b. The girl's masters were unhappy since they'd been using her possession for profit.
9. c. Praying and singing hymns
10. d. Love
11. b. Cheerfully
12. b. Diligence

13. a. The devil
14. c. Spear of discretion
15. b. gain
16. b. Christ Jesus
17. c. Pray about everything
18. c. God
19. c. Christ
20. c. Luke

QUIZ 1E—3

1. c. saved.
2. b. Paul
3. b. He made tents.
4. b. Ephesus
5. b. receive.
6. d. Christianity
7. c. A snake that fastened on his hand (Acts 28:3-6)
8. c. eat
9. a. young
10. b. The love of money
11. a. All Scripture
12. c. Jesus
13. c. Faith
14. b. Moses
15. a. Abraham
16. b. Abraham
17. a. dead
18. c. He will flee from you.
19. c. The devil
20. b. God

QUIZ 1F—1

1. b. Thebes
2. b. Moses' sister, presumably Miriam, to Pharaoh's daughter
3. b. Daisy
4. a. At the burning bush
5. c. The Babylonian army conquered Jerusalem.

6. b. Pharaoh
7. b. She was Jewish.
8. d. Joseph
9. b. Philadelphia
10. a. Their father Isaac
11. a. Ur
12. b. Joseph, the prisoner
13. a. Aurelius
14. a. Deborah
15. b. The Feast of Tabernacles, or Booths
16. b. David
17. b. Eli
18. b. Nehemiah
19. c. 2 John
20. b. Goliath

MINI-QUIZ: HOW DO YOU MEASURE UP?

1. a. the Old Testament
2. b. not in the Bible
3. a. in the Bible
4. b. not in the Bible
5. c. Bethlehem
6. c. Twelve (Yeah, we know, do you count Judas? Do you count Paul? Do you count Andronicus and Junias from Romans 16:7? It's tough, but let's call it twelve.)
7. b. Jesus
8. Matthew, Mark, Luke, and John
9. (1) You shall have no other gods before me.
    (2) You shall not make for yourself an idol (graven image).
    (3) You shall not misuse the name of the Lord your God (take it in vain).
    (4) Remember the Sabbath day by keeping it holy.
    (5) Honor your father and your mother.
    (6) You shall not murder.
    (7) You shall not commit adultery.
    (8) You shall not steal.

(9) You shall not give false testimony (bear false witness/lie).
(10) You shall not covet.

QUIZ 1F—2: EXCUSES

1.   c. Adam
2.   b. Eve
3.   b. Laban
4.   a. Aaron
5.   d. Saul
6.   b. Saul
7.   a. Elijah
8.   d. A nameless servant in one of Jesus' parables
9.   c. Jesus
10.   c. Paul

MINI-QUIZ: WEATHER MATCHING

1.   d. Flood
2.   j. Famine
3.   g. Wind
4.   i. Hail
5.   a. Bright cloud
6.   c. Sun standing still
7.   h. Dew
8.   f. Drought
9.   b. Whirlwind
10.   e. Storm

MINI-QUIZ: WORDS AND PHRASES

1.   c. Turn the other cheek.
2.   a. Spare the rod and spoil the child.
3.   b. Salt of the earth
4.   c. Thorn in the flesh
5.   d. The

MINI-QUIZ: WATER
1. Noah
2. Peter
3. Moses
4. Isaac
5. Mary
6. Jonah

MINI-QUIZ: FEET
1. b. Moses
2. c. Peter and John
3. b. The Prodigal Son
4. c. Her hair
5. a. John the Baptist
6. b. Those who bring good news
7. c. Peter

MINI-QUIZ: PEOPLE WHO PRAYED
1. d. Jacob
2. b. Joshua
3. f. Elisha
4. i. Hezekiah
5. a. Peter
6. h. Paul and Silas

MINI-QUIZ: PEOPLE WHO CRIED
1. c. Esau
2. h. David
3. a. Naomi
4. j. Elisha
5. f. Joseph
6. g. Mary Magdalene
7. b. Jesus
8. d. Peter
9. i. Moses
10. e. Jonathan

QUIZ 2A—1

1. c. It is not good for the man to be alone.
2. a. They would die.
3. c. The serpent
4. c. The flood
5. b. They were his sons.
6. c. A raven and a dove
7. c. He confused their speech, so they "babbled" to one another.
8. b. Abraham
9. a. She laughed out loud.
10. a. The earth
11. b. All he had made
12. d. Eve
13. a. Shepherd
14. d. "Am I my brother's keeper?"
15. b. The number of years he lived
16. b. Abraham
17. b. Lot
18. a. She looked back at the city of Sodom as it was being destroyed.
19. c. Cooking
20. c. He loved to eat red stew (Gen. 25:30). But give yourself half-credit for a—he *was* red (Gen. 25:25).

MINI-QUIZ: FAMOUS FIRSTS

1. Cain
2. Abel
3. God, who "planted a garden in Eden"
4. Noah
5. Green (the plants God created

QUIZ 2A—2

1. c. Esau was trying to kill him.
2. a. Work for Laban for seven years
3. b. He had actually married Rachel's sister, Leah.
4. a. The sun, moon, and stars bowing down to Joseph's star

5.   c. Selling him as a slave
6.   b. He was falsely accused of attacking his master's wife.
7.   b. Pharaoh's baker and cup-bearer
8.   b. Joseph
9.   a. Making bricks and mortar
10. c. He killed an Egyptian slave master for mistreating an Israelite.
11. b. His brother, Aaron
12. c. A snake
13. c. He stopped giving the Israelites straw to make bricks.
14. a. The Nile River turned to blood.
15. c. The Jordan River (Ha! It said "Joshua," not "Moses"!)
16. b. Eight
17. c. Making an idol for the people to worship
18. a. "Do not worship any other gods besides me."
19. b. The ark of the covenant
20. b. He threw the stone tablets of the law to the ground and broke them.

QUIZ 2A—3

1.   b. Aaron
2.   b. His face glowed.
3.   d. Balaam's donkey
4.   b. Because they refused to enter the Promised Land when they had the chance
5.   a. The Day of Atonement
6.   b. Moses
7.   a. heart, all your soul, and all your strength.
8.   b. The water stopped flowing so they could cross on dry ground.
9.   c. She hid two Israelite spies from the king of Jericho.
10. b. Othniel, Ehud, and Shamgar
11. b. Jacob's sons to their brother Joseph
12. c. She killed Sisera by driving a tent peg through his head.
13. b. Make a lamb's fleece wet with dew but the ground dry, then the opposite
14. d. If you're timid or afraid, go home.

15. a. He took them to a stream and watched how they drank water.
16. b. He tied the foxes' tails together around torches and sent them through the fields.
17. c. A donkey's jawbone
18. b. Judges
19. a. He was a distant relative who eventually married her.
20. c. Naomi

QUIZ 2B—1
1. a. He warned against it.
2. b. Saul
3. c. Samuel
4. a. Samuel
5. c. A prophet poured oil on his head.
6. b. David
7. c. Jonathan
8. b. David
9. c. He wanted to talk with the spirit of Samuel.
10. a. With kindness, as his own son
11. c. Bathing on her roof
12. b. To cover up the adultery David had committed
13. b. David, accused of adultery and murder
14. a. He got his long hair caught in a tree and was found by enemy soldiers.
15. b. Solomon
16. c. Solomon
17. b. Solomon
18. c. Jeroboam
19. b. Jeroboam, Menahem, Hoshea
20. c. Jotham, Ahaz, Asa

QUIZ 2B—2
1. c. Elijah
2. b. Assyria
3. c. Hezekiah
4. b. Ravens brought it to him.
5. c. Raised the boy back to life

6. a. Calling fire from heaven to consume their sacrifice
7. b. He dug a trench around the altar and poured water over everything.
8. d. Gentle whisper
9. b. A vineyard
10. a. She trumped up charges against Naboth and had him stoned to death.
11. a. He threw some flour in.
12. d. Sold the oil to pay her debts
13. a. Elisha
14. b. He asked Naaman to pay for the healing and took the payment as his own.
15. b. An ax head that had fallen into the river
16. c. The angel of the Lord killed 185,000 Assyrian soldiers.
17. c. Joash and Josiah
18. a. The Book of the Law
19. b. Baal, Chemosh, and Molech
20. b. Babylon

QUIZ 2B—3
1. b. Nebuchadnezzar
2. c. The altar in Solomon's temple
3. b. Solomon
4. c. Solomon
5. b. The people of the northern kingdom of Israel
6. b. Cyrus
7. a. The return from captivity and rebuilding of the temple
8. c. Elijah
9. d. He called bears out of the woods to maul them.
10. c. Baldhead.
11. a. Haggai and Zechariah
12. c. Ezra (Ezra 7:27-8)
13. b. Nehemiah
14. c. The wall of Jerusalem
15. b. Esther
16. c. She wouldn't come when he called.
17. b. Asked the king to spare her people

18. a. Mordecai
19. a. Ezra, Nehemiah, Esther
20. b. Purim

QUIZ 2C—1

1. c. Job
2. c. Job (Job 1:21)
3. d. His wife
4. d. Buffalo
5. a. Asaph
6. a. The words of his mouth and the thoughts of his heart
7. c. whom shall I fear?
8. a. that the Lord is good.
9. b. an ever-present help in trouble.
10. c. After he had committed adultery
11. b. Renew a right spirit within me.
12. b. rest in the shadow of the Almighty.
13. a. A new song
14. c. It became the cornerstone.
15. c. the work of the builders is useless.
16. b. beside the rivers of Babylon
17. c. The sin hidden deep in my heart
18. b. In my mother's womb
19. d. The Lord
20. b. Praise the Lord! (Hallelujah!)

MINI-QUIZ: PROVERBS

1. e. and not be burned? (6:27).
2. h. but a bold reproof promotes peace (10:10).
3. a. is like a gold ring in a pig's snout (11:22).
4. f. others who are rich pretend to be poor (13:7).
5. d. then brags about getting a bargain! (20:14).
6. b. Don't eat too much of it, or it will make you sick! (25:16).
7. j. You will heap burning coals on their heads, and the Lord will reward you (25:21-22).
8. c. is as dangerous as a thornbush brandished by a drunkard (26:9).

9. i. is someone who lies to a friend and then says, "I was only joking" (26:18-19).
10. g. it will be counted as a curse! (27:14).

QUIZ 2C—2

1. c. The ant
2. c. trusted
3. b. She quilts her own bedspreads.
4. c. Food
5. b. Your nose is a proud watchtower over your face, like the turret of David. (It's the *neck* that is "as stately as the tower of David.")
6. b. love
7. b. Angels with six wings
8. b. the word of our God
9. a. The Servant
10. c. Jeremiah
11. b. God
12. a. He wrote another.
13. b. Ezekiel
14. c. Honey
15. a. The bones began to connect and become living people.
16. c. Each of the four walls of the new city of God
17. b. Daniel and his three friends
18. c. Iron and clay
19. a. A blazing furnace
20. b. His kingdom would be conquered by the Medes and Persians.

QUIZ 2C—3

1. a. He wouldn't stop praying, even when it was made illegal.
2. c. Hosea
3. b. Fat cows
4. b. Nineveh
5. a. He prayed.
6. b. They repented of their sin.
7. c. He was angry that God let such a wicked city repent.

8. c. A great ruler will come from Bethlehem.
9. a. he is a strong refuge.
10. b. Habakkuk
11. c. Jeremiah
12. d. humbly
13. b. work
14. a. my Spirit
15. a. He hates it.
16. b. Elijah
17. c. King Nebuchadnezzar
18. b. Ezekiel
19. b. The destruction of Jerusalem by the Babylonians
20. c. Jonah

QUIZ 2D—1

1. b. In a dream
2. a. Herod
3. b. He could not speak.
4. c. Elizabeth
5. c. They hurried to Bethlehem to see for themselves.
6. a. Eastern lands
7. a. Nazareth
8. b. Twelve
9. c. About thirty
10. b. Camel hair and leather
11. c. Locusts and wild honey
12. a. The Holy Spirit and fire
13. c. To be tempted by the devil
14. b. Every word that comes from the mouth of God
15. c. Away by yourself, with the door closed
16. a. God and money
17. d. Birds
18. c. They will trample them.
19. c. Do unto others as you would have them do unto you.
20. a. A fever

MINI-QUIZ: BEATITUDES
1. c or g. for theirs is the kingdom of heaven
2. f. for they will be comforted
3. a. for they will inherit the earth
4. d. for they will be filled
5. h. for they will be shown mercy
6. b. for they will see God
7. e. for they will be called sons of God
8. g or c. for theirs is the kingdom of heaven

QUIZ 2D—2
1. b. The prince of demons
2. b. His disciples
3. a. The mustard seed
4. c. Yeast
5. a. Both fall into a ditch.
6. c. Moses and Elijah
7. a. Three shrines or shelters
8. a. From the mouth of a fish
9. d. Jesus is there with them.
10. d. Seventy times seven
11. a. Little children
12. b. Go and sell all you have
13. c. Sheep and goats
14. a. Jesus sent them into a herd of pigs.
15. b. sick people do.
16. d. They spread his fame all over the region.
17. a. The Pharisees
18. b. On the Sabbath
19. a. Peter, James, and John
20. c. Theophilus

QUIZ 2D—3
1. b. James and John
2. b. Jesus
3. a. They considered it blasphemy because only God can forgive sins.

4. c. New wineskins
5. b. The word of God
6. c. The feeding of the five thousand
7. b. Twelve basketfuls
8. c. The evils from inside one's heart
9. b. "This is my beloved Son. Listen to him."
10. b. A den of robbers
11. a. David's
12. b. The magnificent buildings of the temple
13. a. Two small copper coins
14. b. It was all she had.
15. a. Lazarus
16. b. All the kingdoms of the world
17. c. "It is not the healthy who need a doctor, but the sick."
18. b. Sat down and said, "This Scripture has come true today before your very eyes!" (Luke 4:21).
19. b. Jesus raised the dead person—a widow's only son—back to life.
20. a. "Where is your faith?"

QUIZ 2D—4

1. b. Followers who traveled with Jesus and supported him
2. b. Call down fire from heaven to destroy it
3. c. Martha
4. a. The door will be opened.
5. a. Pharisees
6. a. Sparrows
7. b. The Sabbath
8. b. Jerusalem
9. c. Begged at the rich man's gate
10. c. The dogs
11. a. Abraham's side
12. b. The rich man who had ignored Lazarus
13. c. Jesus
14. c. He was a tax collector.
15. b. The Samaritan woman at the well
16. a. John the Baptist

17. c. I am a voice shouting in the wilderness, "Prepare a straight pathway for the Lord's coming!"
18. a. "Look! There is the Lamb of God."
19. b. At night
20. d. so that everyone who believes in him will not perish but have eternal life.

QUIZ 2D—5

1. a. He asked her for a drink of water.
2. c. He was Jewish, and Jews did not normally associate with Samaritans.
3. b. The Samaritan woman to her townspeople
4. d. Every so often an angel stirred up the water, giving it healing power.
5. a. Make him king
6. b. His brothers
7. a. He began to write on the ground with his finger.
8. c. Jesus
9. b. A woman captured in the act of adultery
10. b. Abraham
11. c. The devil
12. b. He put mud on the man's eyes and told him to wash in the pool of Siloam.
13. a. There would be a bad odor.
14. b. He dipped a piece of bread in the dish and gave it to that disciple.
15. b. Zacchaeus
16. a. Andrew, Thomas, Judas
17. c. Ten
18. b. One
19. c. weak
20. b. They fell asleep.

QUIZ 2D—6: PASSION WEEK

1. a. This cup of suffering
2. c. Jesus
3. d. His ear

4. b. Peter, about Jesus
5. c. Nicodemus
6. c. Thomas
7. b. The sign on Jesus' cross, calling him King of the Jews
8. a. His seamless robe
9. c. Jesus
10. d. Jesus
11. c. Darkness fell across the whole land.
12. c. A Roman centurion at Jesus' crucifixion
13. d. The disciples Jesus met on the road to Emmaus
14. b. An angel
15. b. Judas, his betrayer
16. c. He broke down and wept.
17. c. The money changers and merchants in the temple
18. a. Hosanna!
19. a. Thirty pieces of silver
20. a. Sang a hymn

QUIZ 2E—1
1. a. Theophilus
2. c. Pentecost
3. a. Barnabas
4. a. So they could spend more time in prayer and preaching
5. c. Stephen
6. b. Paul (Saul)
7. b. Isaiah
8. a. To arrest some Christians
9. b. Dorcas had died, and they wanted Peter to help her if he could.
10. c. If God says something is OK, don't say it isn't.
11. b. A bright light from heaven
12. b. Saul (Paul)
13. a. fools
14. c. While we were still sinners
15. a. Adam's
16. b. He wanted to do right, but kept doing wrong.
17. d. Nothing in all creation

18. c. Our bodies
19. c. transformed by the renewing of your mind.
20. a. The powerless

QUIZ 2E—2

1.   c. Peter
2.   a. A famine would strike.
3.   a. Herod Agrippa
4.   a. She left Peter standing there as she ran back inside to tell the others.
5.   b. In the synagogue
6.   c. Silas
7.   c. Paul
8.   a. An earthquake shook the place.
9.   b. The Scriptures
10. c. Thessalonica
11. b. Athens
12. d. God
13. c. Stay unmarried to better do the work of the Lord.
14. b. Death
15. a. freedom.
16. c. Unbelievers
17. a. Christ lives in me.
18. d. All of the above
19. b. the cross of our Lord Jesus Christ.
20. c. The wall of hostility

QUIZ 2E—3

1.   c. Paul
2.   b. Aquila and Priscilla
3.   c. Paul
4.   a. To ambush and kill Paul
5.   b. Felix, Festus, and Agrippa
6.   c. Paul
7.   c. King Agrippa
8.   d. All of the above
9.   d. Rome

10. c. Paul
11. c. Let the Holy Spirit fill and control us
12. b. Things that are exciting
13. a. through him who gives me strength.
14. d. All of the above
15. b. A runaway slave Paul was sending back to Philemon
16. c. God
17. b. Do what it says.
18. b. God is faithful and just to forgive and cleanse us.
19. b. This evil world and all it offers
20. b. knock

QUIZ 2F—1

1. b. Joseph to the brothers who sold him as a slave
2. c. Manna
3. c. Ten of the Israelite spies who explored the Promised Land
4. b. Sarah
5. c. Joshua
6. c. Psalms 117–119
7. d. Balaam's donkey
8. a. Carthage
9. a. Sarah, at the birth of her son
10. d. Rhine
11. b. The wife of Potiphar, who bought Joseph as a slave
12. b. A seal used by Jeremiah's scribe, Baruch
13. c. A bird of prey
14. b. Bartholomew
15. c. The two front pillars in Solomon's temple
16. d. This is the longest name in the Bible.
17. a. Matthew
18. b. Obadiah
19. b. King Saul, after he disobeyed God's orders
20. c. Nehemiah

QUIZ 2F—2: BY THE NUMBERS

1. c. healed lepers who returned to thank Jesus.
2. a. spies who recommended that the Israelites invade Canaan.

3. b. days Jonah was in the belly of the fish.
4. a. people the king saw in the fiery furnace.
5. a. Bible books credited to Moses.
6. b. days God took to create things.
7. a. times Naaman was told to dip in the Jordan River.
8. a. people on the ark.
9. c. feet tall, approximately, that Goliath was.
10. d. centuries in which Methuselah lived.
11. a. brothers of Joseph.
12. b. disciples of Jesus.
13. b. the famous "love chapter" of 1 Corinthians.
14. a. total years Jacob worked so he could marry Rachel.
15. b. years God added to Hezekiah's life after he prayed for healing.
16. c. number of Gospels squared.
17. a. pieces of silver the slave traders paid for Joseph.
18. a. pieces of silver Judas got for betraying Jesus.
19. b. years the Israelites wandered in the wilderness.
20. d. years that went by before the Israelites were supposed to free all the slaves.
21. c. the minimum age of widows Timothy was told to put on the "widows' list."
22. a. disciples Jesus sent out two by two.
23. b. years old Sarah was when she bore Isaac.
24. a. soldiers led by a centurion.
25. b. soldiers Gideon used to rout an army of thousands.
26. c. years that one day is like to the Lord.

QUIZ 2F—3: FIND THE BOOK

1. b. Matthew
2. c. Luke
3. b. John
4. b. Leviticus
5. a. Judges
6. b. Psalms
7. c. Hosea
8. c. Revelation

9. b. 1 Kings
10. a. Exodus
11. b. Joshua
12. c. Matthew
13. b. Ecclesiastes
14. a. Luke
15. d. Acts
16. b. 1 Samuel
17. b. Ruth
18. c. Esther
19. b. John
20. b. Proverbs
21. a. Numbers
22. b. Song of Songs

MINI-QUIZ: FAMOUS FIRSTS
1. Cain (Gen. 4:1)
2. Be fruitful and multiply (Gen. 1:28).
3. Rebekah
4. The serpent (Gen. 3:4)
5. Abraham (Gen. 14:18-20)
6. Hunting

QUIZ 2F—4: ANGELS
1. c. A staircase or ladder
2. b. Balaam
3. b. Elijah
4. b. Isaiah
5. c. The blazing furnace
6. a. Lions
7. c. Zechariah
8. a. His temptation
9. c. The stone at the door of Jesus' tomb
10. a. Peter

QUIZ 2F—5: SIBLINGS
1. d. Abraham
2. b. Isaac
3. a. Rachel
4. a. Benjamin
5. c. Ephraim
6. b. Miriam
7. d. Absalom
8. d. Herod
9. a. Simon Peter
10. d. Jesus

MINI-QUIZ: NAME CHANGES
1. e. Israel
2. b. Zaphenath-paneah
3. f. Mara
4. a. Hadassah
5. d. Belteshazzar
6. g. Simon Bar-Jonah
7. h. Saul
8. c. Joseph of Cyprus

QUIZ 3A—1
1. b. Abraham's wife, Sarah
2. a. stars in the sky
3. c. To protect him from violence
4. c. descendants of Adam and Eve
5. a. God took him away.
6. d. Sacrificed some of the animals
7. b. He rained down burning sulfur on them.
8. c. She was a servant girl who bore Abraham's son Ishmael.
9. c. She wasn't getting along with Abraham's wife.
10. d. All of the above
11. c. Both Abraham and Isaac
12. b. His wife, Rebekah
13. d. Dug another well
14. c. They were the only sons of Jacob's favorite wife, Rachel.

15. a. Wrestling with a mysterious man who may have been God himself
16. c. Gave him a tenth of the spoils from the battle
17. b. Giving birth to Benjamin
18. c. Mixed. One would die; the other would be set free.
19. c. Seven years of plenty would be followed by seven years of famine.
20. b. He falsely accused Ben of stealing to see if the brothers would defend him.

QUIZ 3A—2

1. b. He rescued her and her sisters from shepherds and then drew water for their flocks.
2. b. He was standing on holy ground.
3. d. All of the above
4. d. All of the above
5. a. They put blood on their doorposts so the Angel of Death would "pass over" them.
6. b. The Lord opened up a path through the water.
7. d. Played the tambourine
8. b. Throw a branch in it
9. d. What is it?
10. b. So they wouldn't have to gather food on the Sabbath
11. a. Water gushed out.
12. c. Moses' father-in-law
13. b. Two
14. d. Grasshoppers
15. c. Milk and honey
16. c. Joshua and Caleb were the only two spies who recommended entering the Promised Land.
17. d. A gold ring from the golden calf
18. a. To create furnishings for the tabernacle
19. b. The Year of Jubilee
20. b. A bronze snake

MINI-QUIZ: FAMOUS FIRSTS

1. Jacob and Esau
2. Metal
3. She's the first sister mentioned in Scripture.
4. Noah
5. The raven

QUIZ 3A—3

1. b. Cities of refuge
2. c. One-tenth of it
3. b. Babel
4. b. Abraham
5. a. A scarlet rope
6. b. Stole some loot from Jericho
7. a. Levi, because they served as priests for all the tribes
8. c. Joseph
9. b. Two mountains that served as the site for the recommitment ceremony
10. c. "The dagger went so deep that the handle disappeared beneath the king's fat."
11. d. She drove a tent peg through his head.
12. c. To sacrifice the first creature that came out to meet him. (It was his daughter.)
13. a. He would never drink wine or cut his hair.
14. c. He had encountered the carcass of a lion in which bees had made honey.
15. b. David
16. d. He thought she was drunk.
17. c. Their people were getting sick.
18. c. Honor your father and mother. Then you will live a long, full life.
19. d. It's the day God took a break from the hard work of creating.
20. c. Fifty

QUIZ 3B—1

1. c. Saul
2. a. He fell out of his chair and died.
3. c. He performed a prebattle sacrifice himself, which only a priest should do.
4. b. David (They were his older brothers.)
5. a. Delivering bread and cheese to the army
6. b. A tax exemption and his daughter's hand in marriage
7. b. He wasn't used to it.
8. c. and David his ten thousands!
9. b. David jumped aside and apparently kept playing the harp for Saul.
10. b. She put a dummy in bed and said David was too sick to be arrested.
11. b. Jonathan, Saul's son
12. c. Abigail
13. a. So the Philistines would let him live among them for a while
14. c. He touched the ark of the covenant.
15. a. He told him a story about a rich man who stole a poor man's pet lamb.
16. d. Cut the baby in half
17. c. Lumber
18. d. His feet became diseased.
19. b. Bake him a bit of bread first
20. c. Sending rain

QUIZ 3B—2

1. b. She had a continual supply of flour and oil.
2. a. Fire came from heaven to consume them.
3. b. He threw salt in it.
4. a. Horses and chariots of fire surrounding the Arameans
5. b. They became blind.
6. b. Jezebel's
7. c. Athaliah
8. d. He prayed.
9. c. The shadow went backwards on the sundial.

10. b. The Babylonians would eventually carry all those treasures away.
11. c. Jehoshaphat
12. c. He was struck with leprosy because only the priests were allowed to burn incense.
13. a. The exiled Jews returning from captivity
14. b. They wept bitterly.
15. c. Intermarrying with local pagans
16. b. Haman
17. a. Explained God's Law
18. b. Nehemiah
19. a. He told his cousin Esther, who told the king.
20. c. Prime minister

QUIZ 3C—1

1. c. Job
2. a. Carthaginian soldiers sowed salt in his fields.
3. a. A piece of broken pottery
4. c. Sat on the ground with him and said nothing
5. a. The crocodile
6. c. Job
7. a. lest he be angry.
8. b. The Lord, who rules in heaven
9. c. Those who refuse to associate with people of ill repute
10. b. A worm
11. b. The slimy pit, out of the mud and mire
12. c. Clap them
13. a. and greatly to be praised.
14. a. To the Lord's sanctuary
15. b. Moses
16. c. The eagle
17. a. A footstool
18. c. Because he hears and answers prayers
19. a. Arrows in a warrior's hand
20. b. His faithful love endures forever.

QUIZ 3C—2

1. b. The mountaintop
2. c. Believers and unbelievers alike
3. c. Wisdom
4. c. A mouth that utters offensive words
5. b. Contributors to the book of Proverbs
6. d. The government
7. c. How a turtle lives within its shell
8. d. Children
9. c. The Teacher (or Preacher)
10. a. In the days of your youth
11. b. and much study wearies the body.
12. b. The majestic olive tree
13. c. death
14. b. A branch or shoot
15. c. Through the desert
16. b. A childless woman
17. d. drink
18. b. Make sinners righteous
19. d. Priests and criminals will join in singing praises.
20. a. To a shop where a potter worked

QUIZ 3C—3

1. b. Babylon
2. b. It would become "an desolate wasteland."
3. b. Baruch
4. c. A shepherd
5. b. Magog
6. c. The writing on the wall seen by Belshazzar
7. b. Israel had been unfaithful to God, but he still loved them.
8. b. tear your hearts.
9. a. Tending sheep
10. b. Edom
11. c. Nineveh
12. c. Rome
13. b. Shepherd
14. a. A fountain

15. a. Sun of Righteousness
16. b. Jonah
17. c. Jehozaphad the Blusterite
18. c. Isaiah
19. c. Job (Job 38:2-4)
20. b. Jeremiah

MINI-QUIZ: ISAIAH 40:31

1. c. will find new strength.
2. f. on wings like eagles.
3. h. and not grow weary.
4. a. and not faint.

QUIZ 3D—1

1. c. God with us
2. b. King Herod was searching for the child to kill him.
3. c. He gave orders to kill all the boys in Bethlehem two years old and under.
4. c. He would have a son, who would become a great prophet.
5. a. Zechariah
6. c. He wrote the baby's name—John—on a tablet, and he could suddenly talk again.
7. c. He had been told that he wouldn't die until he had seen the Messiah.
8. b. Share with one who has none
9. b. Jesus
10. b. The Judean wilderness
11. a. Isaiah
12. a. To prepare the way for Jesus
13. c. The Pharisees and Sadducees
14. a. It would be thrown into the fire.
15. c. Do not test the Lord your God.
16. b. Anger
17. c. Looking lustfully
18. a. What your right hand is doing
19. b. Pale and disheveled
20. b. eye

QUIZ 3D—2

1. c. The lost sheep of Israel
2. a. None
3. d. All things are possible for you if you have clean hands and a pure heart.
4. a. Even though he performed miracles there, they did not repent.
5. b. To destruction
6. a. To life
7. c. By their "fruit," the way they act
8. a. A Roman officer in Capernaum
9. b. A woman who had suffered with a hemorrhage for twelve years
10. b. To heal the daughter of a synagogue leader
11. b. He let the wheat and weeds grow together until harvest.
12. d. John the Baptist, risen from the dead
13. a. Four thousand
14. a. Their false teaching that added to God's law
15. c. Jesus
16. c. "You didn't have enough faith."
17. a. The mother of Zebedee's sons (James and John)
18. b. Jericho
19. b. Said he would work, but didn't
20. a. They were afraid of the crowds.

QUIZ 3D—3

1. b. He (John) was not worthy to stoop down and untie them.
2. b. He taught as one who had real authority, unlike the teachers of the law.
3. a. They knew who he was.
4. b. not man for the Sabbath.
5. d. He is out of his mind.
6. c. Legion, because there were many of them
7. c. The woman who touched Jesus' cloak
8. c. Sheep without a shepherd
9. a. So the people could get something to eat
10. a. They thought they were seeing a ghost.

11. c. Ritual hand washing
12. d. All of the above
13. a. "Get behind me, Satan."
14. b. Which of them was most important
15. d. Only the Father
16. c. Caiaphas
17. b. A woman poured expensive perfume on Jesus' head.
18. b. is for us.
19. c. David
20. c. Establish churches in every land

QUIZ 3D—4

1. c. Don't stop him! Anyone who is not against you is for you.
2. b. Who is my neighbor?
3. b. The Pharisees
4. c. Herod Antipas
5. b. At the foot of the table
6. c. The poor, the crippled, the lame, and the blind
7. c. ninety-nine
8. b. He humbled himself.
9. b. "If they kept quiet, the stones along the road would burst into cheers!"
10. c. He said, "Destroy this temple, and in three days I will raise it up" (meaning his body).
11. a. He healed the son of a government official.
12. a. Bethesda
13. b. Peter
14. c. Simon Peter
15. b. A man being born blind
16. a. Parents of the formerly blind man, being grilled by authorities
17. a. "May no one ever eat your fruit again!"
18. d. We don't know.
19. b. He was killed.
20. b. They were afraid of the crowds.

QUIZ 3D—5: PASSION WEEK

1. b. "My God, My God, why have you forsaken me?"
2. a. Sour wine
3. b. The curtain in the temple
4. c. Each of Jesus' disciples, when Jesus said one of them would betray him
5. c. He had a seal put on the stone door and posted a guard.
6. b. The Garden of Gethsemane
7. a. The Lord needs it and will return it soon.
8. b. Elijah
9. b. Insurrection and murder
10. c. It was the Sabbath.
11. b. Pilate
12. b. A gardener
13. a. On the Mount of Olives
14. b. Peter
15. c. Emmaus
16. d. They thought it was nonsense.
17. b. Empty linen wrappings
18. a. He washed his hands and declared he was innocent of Jesus' blood.
19. c. A scarlet robe, a crown of thorns, and a staff in his right hand
20. a. The Place of the Skull

QUIZ 3E—1

1. b. They would select another disciple to take his place.
2. c. When they spoke in tongues at Pentecost
3. b. That Jesus' miraculous birth had been announced by angels
4. c. Peter and John
5. a. Peter and John
6. b. They had lied about how much they were giving.
7. c. Leave them alone—Christianity will only grow if God is behind it.
8. b. Blasphemy
9. b. Sorcerer
10 b. The Ethiopian eunuch, in the desert with Philip

11. c. Jesus, in a vision from heaven
12. b. Abraham
13. a. condemnation
14. b. The Holy Spirit
15. c. Love
16. a. Paul, Peter (Cephas), Apollos
17. b. what God has prepared for those who love him.
18. b. beneficial.
19. c. Because he once persecuted the church of God
20. c. useless

QUIZ 3E—2

1. a. A position as one of the twelve disciples, replacing Judas
2. b. The lame man healed by Peter and John
3. d. All of the above
4. c. He couldn't see.
5. d. In a basket, over the city wall
6. c. Dorcas
7. a. Meditating on the roof
8. a. James
9. c. Paul got up and went back into the city.
10. b. Whether Gentile believers should be required to convert to Judaism
11. a. Barnabas wanted to take Mark with them; Paul didn't.
12. c. Now it's time to forgive him and comfort him.
13. c. Jars of clay
14. b. Refused to eat with Gentiles when the legalists were present
15. a. to do good works, which God prepared in advance for us to do.
16. d. All of the above
17. a. Men
18. c. Those who are rich in this world
19. d. All of the above
20. b. Because of his mercy

MINI-QUIZ: FAMOUS FIRSTS

1. Stephen (Acts 6–8:1)
2. A wedding at Cana (John 2:1-11)
3. Saul (Paul) (Acts 13:2)
4. Christians (Acts 11:26)
5. James (Acts 12:1-2)

QUIZ 3E—3

1. c. Saul (Paul)
2. c. He had abandoned them, going home early during their first journey.
3. b. Lydia
4. c. A jailer in Philippi
5. a. Apollos
6. c. Burned them
7. c. Silversmith
8. b. Jesus
9. a. Paul's belt
10. b. Blasphemed the temple by bringing a Gentile inside
11. d. By declaring his Roman citizenship
12. b. Agrippa
13. a. The throne of grace
14. c. The race God has set before us
15. c. Both of those
16. b. Elijah
17. c. Christ
18. a. Give an answer to those who ask the reason for our hope
19. b. The one who is in you
20. b. Corinth

QUIZ 3F—1

1. b. Noah's ark
2. a. When the angel kept Abraham from sacrificing his son Isaac
3. b. To Rebekah, about Jacob and Esau
4. c. Joseph to his brothers
5. c. Arabic
6. d. Moses

7. c. Alexandria
8. a. Moses, after he complained that he was not a skilled speaker
9. b. Jeremiah
10. c. The Israelites passed through the Red Sea, and the Egyptians didn't.
11. c. Hezekiah's tunnel
12. b. Abraham
13. a. David's "mighty men"
14. a. Jacob, to the mysterious being he wrestled with
15. b. David
16. b. Hezekiah
17. c. Isaiah
18. a. Genesis
19. c. Nehemiah to King Artaxerxes (Neh. 2:8)
20. a. Moses

MINI-QUIZ: ANAGRAMS

1. Zechariah
2. Genesis
3. Leviticus
4. Deuteronomy
5. 2 Chronicles
6. Nahum
7. Daniel
8. Hosea

QUIZ 3F—2: FEAR NOT

1. a. Isaac
2. b. Jacob
3. b. Joshua
4. c. The women who came to anoint Jesus' body
5. a. Simon Peter
6. d. Paul
7. d. John
8. b. Zechariah
9. b. Shepherds
10. c. Mary

MINI-QUIZ: GIFTS GIVEN

1. b. Jacob
2. b. Hannah
3. c. The queen of Sheba
4. b. Jesus
5. a. Jonathan

QUIZ 3F—3: MOUNTAINS

1. Noah's ark
2. Abraham
3. Sinai
4. Moses
5. Joshua
6. Deborah
7. Elijah
8. David
9. Jesus
10. Elijah

MINI-QUIZ: WEDDINGS

1. a. Leah
2. b. Samson
3. b. Ezra
4. c. Cana
5. a. The people he invited didn't come.
6. d. Oil for their lamps
7. c. Revelation

CHALLENGE QUIZ 3F—4: DREAMERS

1. Jacob
2. Pharaoh
3. The magi (wise men)
4. Joseph's
5. Paul
6. Solomon
7. Daniel

8. Joseph
9. Peter
10. Pentecost
11. Daniel
12. Pilate
13. Saul (Paul)
14. Joseph
15. Gideon
16. Ezekiel
17. Psalms (126:1)
18. Peter

QUIZ 3F—5: FIND THE BOOK

1. b. Matthew
2. c. 1 John
3. c. Galatians
4. b. Daniel
5. c. 1 Timothy
6. b. Jeremiah
7. a. Romans
8. b. Micah
9. c. Revelation
10. b. Acts
11. a. Zechariah
12. b. Luke
13. c. John
14. b. Acts
15. a. Ezekiel
16. c. Romans
17. b. Daniel
18. c. 1 Corinthians
19. a. Hebrews
20. c. James
21. b. Isaiah
22. a. Genesis